LEAVING
HUMANITY

The Corrupt Designs Of Technocratic Elites

by

JOE DORAN

ebook
ISBN-13: 979-8-9859049-2-5

paperback
ISBN-13: 979-8-9859049-3-2

About the Author

JOE DORAN currently contributes to the **Trends Journal**, a leading forecasting magazine published by Gerald Celente. His work has also appeared in Wine Press News, King World News and elsewhere.

Joe has written regional business and human interest articles for the *Hudson River View* since 2018. Previously he published a regional politics focused newsletter, *The Right Stuff*.

In the 1990's Joe covered sports for the *Kingston Daily Freeman*, and before that, he worked as a reporter for *The Poughkeepsie Journal*.

Joe is also a creative writer who has written movie scripts, stage plays and other works.

Most recently he wrote and produced *The Fiddle Faddles Christmas Special*, a retro-style animated holiday program.

His screenplay *Shut-In Santas* earned finalist in the 2020 Screenplay Festival (Sherman Oaks, CA), as well as STORYPROS semi-finalist (2019). His screenplay *Need A Little Christmas* was selected for the 2019 Great Lakes Christian Film Festival. It placed semi-finalist in STORYPROS screenplay competition (2018), quarter-finalist in the PAGE Awards (2018). A previous screenplay, *Twice Loved*, a story about a scientist's attempt to regain his daughter in the wake of a tragic accident by cloning her, was optioned in 1997 by actor John Ritter.

Joe has several stage plays published and available via booksellers, including *Lying Fallow* and *Permanent Things*, written in the 1990's. Joe's radio plays have aired on Western Public Radio, the Armed Forces Radio Network in Europe, and have been performed by theatre groups across the country. As an actor, playwright and theatre producer, he worked with many companies and professionals.

A 1991 Vassar College Powerhouse Playwriting alumnus, Joe studied with Jon Robin Baitz, and went on to co-found two highly regarded regional theatre companies, High Window and Passionplace.

As a theatre director, Joe has worked with Pulitzer and Tony Award winning playwright/screenwriters Frank D. Gilroy (*The Subject Was Roses*) and David Rabe (*Hurlyburly, The Firm, Streamers*). He directed a production of Mr. Rabe's unpublished play *Cosmologies* at the Julien J. Studley Theatre in New Paltz, NY, starring Michael C. Williams (*The Blair Witch Project*).

Joe produced and directed staged readings for the 1996 and 1997 Hudson Valley Film Festivals, featuring Dennis Farina, Charles Durning, Joanna Kerns, Chris Noth, Dan Lauria and others.

As an actor, Joe performed in many regional productions, including *The Lisbon Traviata* at the Egg in Albany, and *Waiting For Godot* at the International Festival of Cafe Theatre in Nancy, France. He also played Biff opposite Dominic Chianese (The Sopranos) as Willy Loman in *Death Of A Salesman*.

Joe has a live and let live attitude. He believes humans and sinners (which are one and the same) should have requisite humility, and not try to control or remake others, much less the entire human race.

He grew up on 70's drive-in flicks, read tons of sci-fi and comics, is a Rifftrax and MST3K junkie, prefers average erotica to Hollywood gore any day of the week, is a songwriter who plays guitar and a little piano, and had a blast in his college days as a bassist in a local 80's new wave band.

Joe has several children and lives with his long-time partner in the beautiful Hudson Valley region of NY.

TABLE OF CONTENTS

FORWARD by Gerald Celente

The King's James Bible got it wrong. Or maybe it was a typo.

It's not "Blessed are the meek, for they shall inherit the Earth."

The Geeks, "a person that is socially awkward... a person of an intellectual bent that is disliked by others," have inherited the earth.

The Geeks have transformed every aspect of 21st century life, and it's just the beginning. There is virtually no corner of human existence that has not been directly and powerfully affected by the Geek created techno-world.

Lacking style and grace, from Steve Jobs to Mark Zuckerbergs of Geekworld, the only thing that's changed in a generation is the color of their T-shirts... from black to blue.

Geeks have replaced the soul of human musicians and the voices that belted out songs with passion and heart, with computerized programming that embodies the passionless personalities they personify.

Across the spectrum—algorithms have replaced heartbeats. The human spirit and emotions have been diluted and technosized.

"Think for yourself" has been lost to Geek control that does the thinking, solves simple and complex problems, educates, writes, spells, does the numbers, intellectualizes, sexualizes, drives artistic impulses and ultimately decides what's worthy and relevant.

Their AI/VR technologies will sweep industries, households and governments worldwide. More and more jobs will be replaced by robotics and AI programs will become, in effect, virtual human beings; they'll take tests, advance their knowledge base through trial and error, perform complex human functions and learn from their mistakes and failures.

They'll get degrees, honors and salutations along the way, and become motivated to become more "human" as we become less human.

Joe Doran's book contains insights, analysis and articles that focus in many ways the disconnect between technological "progress" and human betterment.

We have entered into the galaxy of the New World Disorder... a New ABnormal.

It is all about the bottom line of money and control.

Scientists and technocrats are observing no bounds in their quest to profit from every dimension of technological innovations. As they dissolve more and more of the human spirit, their benefit is about themselves, what they own and how much they can own the mind, body and spirit of what was once humanity.

COVID War

Need more proof?

Go back to January 2020 when, in celebration of its Chinese Lunar New Year, The Year of the Rat, the COVID War was launched from Wuhan, China.

Among the many weapons politicians and scientists used to beat the virus was to force the Operation Warp Speed gene therapy inoculations into the human body... the first ever.

And who were the first businesses to forbid the employees to come to work?

The Geek Gang... the Silicon Valley technocrats who handsomely profited as the world went *Zoom* and tech stocks skyrocketed to unimaginable highs and hundreds of millions of lives and livelihoods were destroyed.

And how dare you dispute what they say or believe what you believe despite having the facts, data and science to disprove the Geeks?

If you did—or still do, be it the COVID War, Ukraine War or any "official government policy"—artificial intelligence-driven censorship and surveillance, weaponized robotics and AI, etc., will shut you down... and in the future, may lock you up.

They are the Police: Every breath you take, every move you make, every step you take, every word you say, every game you play... they'll be watching you.

Inhumanism 2.0

 In the inhuman tech-sense, technology has been uncoupled from true human advancement.

Transhumanists take pains to profess that their goals are to improve humanity. But their works speak differently.

They have a dim view of natural humanity or natural immunity.

Their goals and pursuits are anti-human, or at least anti most of the human population. Many of their experiments are wildly dangerous, and their implementations of de-humanizing technologies should give us all pause. But for the masses, just as they obediently marched off to the COVID War, they will obey their tech-masters whose technology sets new standards for artificial "imagination."

The details presented by Joe Doran will serve as an alarm that goes to the core issue that has to be faced: people should be extremely suspicious and aware of the dangers when it comes to internalizing "progress" by attempting to transcend our natural human selves... the body, blood and spirit of our Divine creator.

We are endowed by our Creator with the unalienable Rights of Life, Liberty and the Pursuit of Happiness. Only you have a right to decide whether anyone should have that power and tell you who you should be, what you should believe, what you should know.

Clearly, via technologies of genetics and bio-pharma, and Artificial Intelligence and robotics, technocrats are racing to profit not only by fundamentally changing our world, but literally who and what we are.

Perhaps the overall point of this book is to illustrate that the decision of restoring the human spirit of Life on Earth and aspiring to ascend to higher spirits must be made now... or descend into the Metaverse.

Gerald Celente, March 2022

INTRODUCTION

This book contains articles that focus in different ways on the disconnect between technological and human progress.

Scientists and technocrats are observing no bounds in their quest to profit in one way or another from technological innovations. In doing so, they're not fundamentally concerned with benefiting human beings, or even preserving natural humanity itself.

Forced gene therapies have provided an excellent example, along with artificial intelligence-driven censorship and surveillance, weaponized robotics and AI, etc. In a real sense, technology has been uncoupled from true human advancement.

Transhumanists take pains to profess that their goals are to improve humanity. But their works speak differently.

They have a dim view of natural humanity, and their goals and pursuits are anti-human, or at least anti most of the human population. Many of their experiments are wildly dangerous, and their de-humanizing technologies should give us all pause.

Thankfully, there are counter-currents in culture and technology which are also touched on in this book. Decentralized, permissionless cryptocurrencies and Web3 technologies in many ways represent an insurgency against entrenched technocratic elites. Of course, those same powerful interests have realized the threat, and are working to co-opt the crypto revolution.

More generally, the COVID War, and now the calamitous Russia-Ukraine conflict have opened many people's eyes concerning the utterly corrupt machinations and power grabs of elites.

Hopefully the information presented here will serve as an alarm that goes to the core issue that has to be faced: people should be extremely wary about the hubris of unbound technocrats, and any "progress" that attempts to transcend our natural human selves.

The Technocracy is racing to profit not only by controlling and fundamentally changing our world, but literally who and what we are. We have a right to decide whether anyone should have that power.

Perhaps the overall point of this book is to illustrate that average humanity needs to assert itself against the dictates of a corrupt and arrogant few, and soon.

Joe Doran, March 2022

TECHNOCRATS DREAM THE TRANSHUMAN NIGHTMARE

THE "PROGRESS" OF LEAVING HUMANS BEHIND

(first published on 1 Jun 2021 in the _Trends Journal_; republished at _KingWorldNews.com_)

The idea that cutting-edge technologies are providing widespread benefits to humankind is failing the test of observation.

The prime current example is new mRNA and DNA COVID "vaccine" technology. They have been lauded for saving the world from a deadly virus. But the world wouldn't have needed saving, if the virus were never created in a bio lab in Wuhan China, which appears more likely than ever.

The Biden Administration was forced to admit last week not only that the COVID-19 might have come from that biolab, but that its release might've been deliberate.

An Out-Of-Control Tech Checklist

There are a number of large-scale examples of how rapid technological advances are benefitting only a relative few, while harming societies and humankind on the whole:

- The build-out of a "social credit" system in China, which comprehensively surveils, penalizes and rewards citizens according to how well they adhere to the dictates of communist masters
- Genetic and chimeric alteration of crops, animals and even humans, with unknown long-term consequences
- Slick social media platforms employing biased algorithms to censor information, opinions and persons, manipulating elections and the free flow of information around the world
- A dangerous growing divide in wealth and power between a relative few controllers of technology and the rest of

humankind, evidenced by the elitist exploitation of pandemic lockdowns
- The development of robotics, drone technologies and AI to conduct overwhelming accurate and lethal kills of human targets
- The use of hormonal and surgical "therapies" to perform controversial gender reassignments of children
- The widespread introductions of man-made chemicals into the environment which have been linked to alarming reductions in fertility rates and sperm counts

Technocratic elites are <u>aware</u> that swiftly advancing technology is not resulting in widespread human betterment. But their only real concern may be to employ technology to control the dissatisfaction of the masses, and indeed, the masses themselves.

Technology Evolving Beyond Constraints Outlined by Game Theory

The pace and direction of technological innovations is reaching the point where existential human issues are at stake. In 2017, a Bloomberg opinion article entitled "How Technology Might Get Out Of Control" predicted some of the issues currently metastasizing.

Into the modern age, the pace of innovation was such that actors could understand and take into account consequences. This social process has been identified and studied in Game Theory. States of "equilibrium" ensured a certain amount of benefit from innovations, while containing disincentives for acting outside the bounds of customs, laws and regulations.

But the article pointed out that emerging technologies were accelerating beyond human social constraints that previously worked:

...emerging technologies -- especially computing, software and biotechnology such as gene editing -- are much more likely to fall into the unstable category. In these areas, disruptions are becoming bigger and more frequent as costs fall and sharing platforms enable open innovation. Hence, such technologies will evolve faster than regulatory frameworks -- at least as traditionally conceived -- can respond.

Given current issues with biotechnology, hi-tech weapons, AI usage in surveillance and control, genetic experimentation and more, the concern of at least some scientists a half decade ago seems to have fully materialized.

The thrust of many projects is solving "problems" created by the existence of humans. We consume too much. We require too much energy. Too much space. We emit too much CO_2. We are selfish, given to superstitious beliefs (ie. religion) and war. We do not contribute anything necessary. We are non-essential.

Little wonder that the tech-fueled proscriptions for dealing with the problems consistently involve more strictly limiting and even effectively removing the source of the problem itself.

From Closeness to Gods to Masters of Tech

Average persons and populations have always been expendable to elites. Status long decided who could be enslaved to build monuments, conscripted in wars, and thrown to the pits to please the gods.

But with the industrial age, no longer did elites have to posit their superiority on mysteries, closeness to the gods, royal blood lines, and connections to the crown.

Science and ideologies based on scientism became the new separators. It was leveraged in the industrial age, and spawned the titans of industry. Along with that age, arose a technocratic apprehension of uselessness of the masses.

Indeed, the systematic human exterminations of the 20th century—the democides that were not wars between countries, but by elites against their own useless populations—were implementations of the new thinking.

And that drive has only grown more sophisticated in the 21st century. Climate change, sustainability, equity. No matter the rhetoric, technologies are not being pursued and funded to sustain, or enlarge the freedoms and prosperity of the bulk of humankind.

Human Limits vs Transcending the Human

One might posit that human nature, and not technology itself, is the real issue. The argument would go something like, "Tech innovations don't harm people. People do."

That might be true for prior history. But it may not hold with evolving AI systems, and genetically modified life forms designed to effectively transcend and replace natural humanity. And that is the frontier that is quickly emerging right now via numerous scientific pursuits around the globe.

Just as human biology is now taken as something that can be transcended, natural humanity itself is quickly becoming a focal point for technocratic "upgrades". It's no mistake that Moderna, one of the companies that created the experimental mRNA COVID vaccines, described their technology as a "human operating system" platform, capable of delivering genetic encoded upgrades.

But Humans 2.0 is not really about upgrading the masses. It's about pursuing god-like powers for a few, and systematically winnowing the rest.

The COVID saga may one day be viewed as a definitive salvo in that technocratic quest. More are on the way.

"UNCONTROLLABLE" AI CLOSE TO REALITY

(first published on 19 Jan 2021 in the *Trends Journal*)

The tech website "Interesting Engineering" referenced an alarming new report by the prestigious Max Planck Society that assessed human's capability for controlling killer Artificial Intelligence technologies. According to the report, science is rapidly approaching the point where AI will effectively break out of human control, something previously only presaged by doomsday blockbuster sci-fi movie franchises like The Matrix and Terminator and the supercomputer HAL from 2001: A Space Odyssey.

The research institute's paper was published last week in the Journal of Artificial Intelligence Research. It explores whether humans will retain the ability to react effectively to a scenario where a "Skynet"-style AI decides it would be in the earth's interest to end humanity.

According to the paper's authors, this is something people need to be thinking about and planning for, in much the same way that other crisis scenarios involving biological weapons, or an EMT event, are game-planned.

"A super-intelligent machine that controls the world sounds like science fiction," study co-author Manuel Cebrian said. But Cebrian believes that AI's capability of making and carrying out impactful decisions for humanity, without answering to any authority beyond itself, is just around the corner.

The report advises the development of a "containment algorithm" that can simulate the dangerous behavior of a super-intelligent AI and prevent it from doing anything harmful. "There are already machines that perform certain important tasks independently without programmers fully understanding how they learned it. The question, therefore, arises whether this could at some point become uncontrollable and dangerous for humanity."

HUMANS SUBJECT TO mRNA "SOFTWARE UPDATES"

(first published on 30 Mar 2021 in the *Trends Journal*)

For anyone who believes the COVID vaccines are a unique phenomenon, guess again.

Moderna, a company on the forefront in developing a COVID vaccine, envisions its mRNA technology as an "operating system" delivering the "software of life," complete with frequent updates. Only with humans as the recipients.

The Moderna website has a page devoted to explaining that mRNA technology is meant to deliver much more to people than just a one-time vaccine. Under the heading, "Our Operating System," complete with a nifty graphic, it explains:

> *Recognizing the broad potential of mRNA science, we set out to create an mRNA technology platform that functions very much like an operating system on a computer. It is designed so that it can plug and play interchangeably with different programs. In our case, the "program" or "app" is our mRNA drug - the unique mRNA sequence that codes for a protein.*

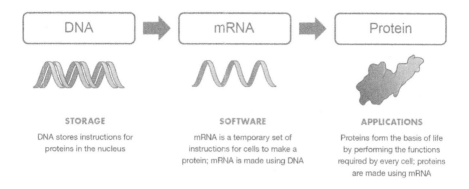

STORAGE	SOFTWARE	APPLICATIONS
DNA stores instructions for proteins in the nucleus	mRNA is a temporary set of instructions for cells to make a protein; mRNA is made using DNA	Proteins form the basis of life by performing the functions required by every cell; proteins are made using mRNA

Those "application" proteins created by Moderna's "operating system," and "software" are designed to occur...inside people.

The Moderna website explains their expansive designs in terms of a "Software of Life" in another section:

> Generally, the only thing that changes from one potential mRNA medicine to another is the coding region – the actual genetic code that instructs ribosomes to make protein. Utilizing these instruction sets gives our investigational mRNA medicines a software-like quality. We also have the ability to combine different mRNA sequences encoding for different proteins in a single mRNA investigational medicine.
>
> We are leveraging the flexibility afforded by our platform and the fundamental role mRNA plays in protein synthesis to pursue mRNA medicines for a broad spectrum of diseases.

If the technology Moderna is touting were strictly voluntary, like traditional medical treatments, that might be one thing. But that very notion is being tested right now in the "crisis" vaccine rollout.

Governments around the world, spurred on and advised by globalist entities such as the World Health Organization, The World Economic Forum, the UN and others, are edging closer and closer to making

COVID vaccines compulsory. There seems little doubt that if that drive meets with no resistance, people are likely to be subject to whatever future "updates" technocratic elites decide are necessary for humankind.

Moderna's language describing its innovations is quite literally de-humanizing. It likens humans to machines, and extols "programming" them to build proteins that trigger other events, whether immunological responses, or "fixes" to diseases. Unfortunately that language is about more than analogies and semantics. It underscores a technocratic view about what humans are, and what boundaries are acceptable in pushing invasive experimental technologies into their bodies.

FOR TECHNOCRATIC ELITES, THERE IS NO "NATURAL"

(first published on 30 Mar 2021 in the _Trends Journal_)

"Man the toolmaker" is an old trope defining what sets humans apart from other creatures. But what happens when what we're changing is ourselves, as well as the world around us?

"Gender fluidity," "transhumanism," chimeric experimentation, radical "Great Resets" and compulsory "mRNA vaccines" can all be seen as facets of the same impulse: disregard for, or outright obliteration of the natural. According to this worldview, what exists is not ultimately fixed or immutably defined. Any aspect of "nature" is malleable to human will, imagination and technology.

Understanding that mindset and modus operandi is key to unlocking the technocratic worldview and proscriptions for "progress."

A recent article by Mathew Lu at the American Mind website explored some of the rationales of the worldview. He noted, "We now live a new 'ethics of modernity' that has habituated nearly all of us to modes of life and ways of being that are fundamentally alienated from human nature as traditionally understood."

Lu argues that changes in mathematics and science, from apprehending an inherent "nature" of reality via geometry, etc. underwent radical re-invention beginning in the enlightenment, and culminating with modern mathematics and science. The new science is all about constructing new solutions, models and realities, as pointed out in works like David Lachterman's Ethics Of Geometry.

As Lu notes about Lachterman's work:

> Modern mathematics "is essentially occupied with the
> solution of problems, not with the proof of theorems," and so,

for the moderns, "mathematics is most fertilely pursued as the 'construction of problems or equations'—that is, as the transposition of mathematical intelligibility and certainty from the algebraic to the geometrical domain, or from the interior forum of the mind to the external forum of space and body." In other words, where the old mathematics described what its practitioners saw as immutable and given in the world around them, in the new mathematics it is the practitioners' ideas that are primary. The culmination of the modern project seek to conform the world to the mind instead of the mind to the world.

An Infinitely Malleable "Reality"?

Lu argues that a view of the world as infinitely malleable has had widespread implications in society and politics, morality and popular culture. Technological innovations have made seemingly impossible things possible.

"Predictive modeling" is used instead of accrued real world data to roll out mass crisis health initiatives such as the worldwide COVID vaccinations. AI-powered algorithms decide what information we access and view. Whole populations are surveilled and assigned credit scores to modify and conform behaviors to the desires of political masters.

Scientists are moving quickly from genetically modifying plants, to modifying people. So-called chimeric experimentation, or mixing the human genome with that of other animals, a scenario evoked by H.G. Wells in *The Island of Dr. Moreau*, is already happening.

In crucial respects, "natural" is no longer considered "inevitable," or even standard.

Lu explained some of the conceits and consequences of the intellectual unbounding of the will from any recognition of limits.

> It is precisely this kind of distancing between model and reality that enables us to even take seriously, much less believe, a "woke" claim like someone is actually a "woman in a man's body." As we become more and more accustomed to living in a world of models, we eventually see ourselves and our own bodies as part of our own self-generated abstractions. This ethos also explains why "intellectuals" were originally more readily drawn into thinking this way than "normal" people. People who work with their hands are much more intimately familiar with the straightforward intransigence of material reality to the human will. Wood, steel, and stone will ultimately yield, but only after a great deal of effort and a deep understanding of their proper natures. Master craftsmen become so only because they accustom themselves to the intrinsic properties of their materials and tools.

Rooted In Delusion

The pretensions of the technocratic mindset to upend notions of the natural as it applies to the sexes, is a current rage. In a piece titled "The War On Sex" Alexander Riley, a Professor of Sociology at Bucknell University, noted:

> But human and nature cannot so easily be pried apart. The evidence of the biological reality of the sex difference—not just in gonads and sex cells, but in personality characteristics and behavioral profiles, on average—is overwhelming, and science is daily producing more. Male and female brains are structurally different in ways that map on to the emerging neuroscientific knowledge on how brain structure affects behavior and capabilities. The feminist claim that these

29

differences are wholly a product of socialization becomes more implausible the more we know. In societies where egalitarian gender ideology is arguably most widespread, such as in Northern Europe, there has been no disappearance of traditional sex differences in choices concerning careers. Men are still overrepresented in fields that focus on systems and objects, and women are still the overwhelming majority in fields dedicated to extensive human interaction and social services.

The article also countered claims that "intersex" individuals (ie. people with some physiological traits of both males and females) was a statistically significant portion of the human population:

The true estimate of intersex individuals, [Physician and Psychologist] Leonard Sax argued, is roughly 0.018%, about 100 times lower than Fausto-Sterling's estimate. That is, more than 99.98% of humans are clearly either male or female in terms of biological sex.

Every New Is Old Again

In important respects, the idea of limitless transcendence, or living without bounds, is hardly new. It's a notion as old as Adam. In the modern age, its conceits have shifted from religious and philosophic, to grounds more typically cloaked in science. Dizzying advances in technology have fueled a sense of inevitably to the technocratic worldview. But can nature really be defied?

Throughout much of history, elites didn't seek so much to deny limits for themselves, as to align themselves with the gods, who were above the lot of average humans. From the Pharaoh, to the "sun king" Louis XIV, to Emperor Hirohito in the 20th century, the authority of Kings to dictate, transgress and live by a different standard was tied to their literal blood connection with deities.

Modernity famously abandoned God. But if anything, the modern technocratic mindset has only accelerated God-like aspirations for humans—or at least a privileged subset. Technocrats regularly envision enhancing themselves in virtually every respect to become, not more human, but less so.

Merging with machines is proposed to gain the mental prowess of super computers, and the strength of robotics. Leveraging information and systems of technocratic control are seen as ways of assuming God-like powers over the average, unwashed (ie. carbon-dirty, over-breeding, over-consuming and now literally virus contaminated) masses. Altering genetics is seen as a path for changing any physiological destiny.

Augmented omniscience, unprecedented societal power over others, and indefinite life extension are all considered not only within reach, but perfectly desirable, by the technocratic elite. What those unbounded desires mean for the rest of us, however, is already progressively spelling, not Utopia, but a hell on earth.

SMART CITIES WILL BE DIGITAL PRISONS

(First published on 30 Mar 2021 in the *Trends Journal*)

To paraphrase Charles Dickens, "It was the best of intentions, it was the worst of ideas…"

Unaccountable, billionaire-funded organizations are leading the charge to "smart cities," designed to comprehensively model behaviors and control activities of inhabitants. That's according to Derek Boze of the Last American Vagabond news blog, and reported in Blacklisted News.

The purpose of the architectural engineering is…well, engineering humans. Lofty-sounding utopian goals include ending "systemic" racism, (ie, racism that can't be established via traditional notions of evidence and common sense), overcrowding (fueled by immigration, not actual American citizen birth rates), and crime (most prevalent in urban areas controlled by leftists peddling further "solutions" like smart cities).

But the actual proscriptions for city designs and "features" are anything but utopian. They would diminish privacy, do away with the dignity and incentives of property ownership, and curtail freedom of movement. If that sounds a lot like the lockdowns of 2020 with some bread and circus bells and whistles, you're getting the idea.

Billionaires like Bill Gates, Jeff Bezos via his media mouthpiece *The Washington Post*, George Soros, Klaus Schwab and partners at the UN all have a hand in pushing the Smart City agenda. In fact, it's part of the so-called "Great Reset", predicated on a very old communist paradigm.

The radical fever-dreams of Marx and acolytes like Vladimir Lenin systematically rejected everything of the organically established, evolved order of life. The motivating epicenter of their history-poisoning cult has always been to "make everything new," according to the artificial mental constructs created by their grandiose and often tragically absurd visions.

And "making everything new," dressed up with technocratic capabilities and innovations, is what the Great Reset and the Smart City are all about.

As Derek Boze outlines:

> A Smart City is promoted as an urban environment which 'uses data and emerging technologies to improve the quality of life for citizens, share information with the public, drive economic growth and build a more inclusive society'. This city would involve the use of technologies such as Internet of Things (IoT), artificial intelligence, and drones to 'improve citizens' lives and solve the challenges of today while preparing to address those of tomorrow.

What could go wrong with a human existence monitored by drones and artificial intelligence, where all actions are digitally captured and used to decide and dictate allowed behaviors and activities? Everything, when one considers that smart cities are really designed to further separate the masters of the universal who control it, from those being controlled.

Quickly Being Prototyped And Rolled Out

"Smart Cities" aren't just fodder for books, whitepapers and conjecture. Components and protocols are being designed and even implemented right now. In November 2020, not wasting the opportunities presented by the largely elite manufactured COVID crisis, the WEF selected 36 cities to "pioneer a new global policy roadmap for smart cities developed by the G20 Global Smart Cities Alliance" (GSCA).

Pioneer cities include Barcelona, Spain; Buenos Aires, Argentina; Dubai, United Arab Emirates; London, United Kingdom; Mexico City, Mexico, and San José, United States.

A major feature of the Smart City is the invasive use of technology to surveil, control and collect information from citizens. As described by the GSCA:

> To support their booming urban populations, many cities have come to rely on the internet of things (IoT)—that is, the world's ever-expanding network of connected devices—to collect, share and analyze real-time data on urban environments. The data gathered using IoT technologies is helping these "smart cities" to combat crime, reduce pollution, decrease traffic congestion, improve disaster preparedness and more. However, it is also raising growing concerns about privacy, security and other risks.

What's not built into the technological surveillance and data collection envisioned by the "pioneering" program? Traditional Constitutional limits on privacy or respect and attention to legal, long established human freedoms.

Other components of the Smart City include controlling human activities via "sustainable development" and considerations of "equity." These terms really mean limiting the ability of average people to work, innovate and create wealth for themselves, and controlling what wealth they do manage to create.

In that vein, living quarters, the ability to acquire and use land, and the ability to transact freely for mutual benefit to accrue wealth and satisfy desires and demands of fellow citizens will no longer be in the hands of citizens themselves. The idea of contracting and interacting in relative freedom isn't a feature of the Smart City.

As for the governance of the comprehensive impositions? Well, that would be handled by the GSCA and the WEF of course, funneled down to local authorities. Think of the "comprehensive plan" rubric, familiar to anyone who has attended a few local town or city council meetings over the past two decades. These proscriptions from higher authorities and funders have radically changed the process of deciding land use and regulations from a citizen to local legislator approach, to a higher authority to local legislator system of control.

And the top-down, undemocratic design of the Smart City is perhaps the ultimate tell that the whole concept isn't really about improving the lives of average citizens. They really have no say or input, regarding the far away, global entities and authorities designing and pushing it.

The mega powerful technocratic elites, and privileged political and government authorities won't be subject to the same limitations and protocols, as the inhabitants trapped in the dystopian landscape of AI-powered city prisons. They almost certainly won't be the ones living in them. They will have grand escapes, with scads of private property, and total privacy.

The goal of the Smart City is to systematically reduce, in the near future term, the nuisance of non-essential masses, given to over-consuming, and defiling the earth via physical occupation and despoliation, carbon emissions, spread of disease, etc.

And in the only slightly longer scheme of things, perhaps via genetic intervention and more explicit and stringent birth rate control, the Smart City is really designed to eliminate the problem entirely.

BIG CHANGES IN 2021: CRISPR CREATOR SAYS GENE EDITING JUST GETTING STARTED

(first published on 22 Jun 2021 in the *Trends Journal*)

Don't worry about humans gene-editing themselves and everything else. It will all turn out positive.

That's the view of one of the scientists who created the CRISPR technology being used to create genetically modified food—and now —people.

Dr. Jennifer Doudna was quoted in an April article on the website Freethink proselytizing for technology she helped invent in 2012. The interview occurred before the re-examination of the possible origins of the COVID-19 virus heated up.

A growing number of people, including some prominent scientists who've examined the virus, now believe it may well have been constructed in a Wuhan China biolab, using CRISPR. But so far at least, few in government or media are expressing outrage or calling for moratoriums on the worldwide use of such technology.

In the Freethink interview, Doudna expressed overall optimism that gene manipulation would be a boon, not only curing genetic diseases, but addressing climate change and even societal issues of "equity." She expressed little concern about the possibility of unforeseen catastrophes.

Concerning the general impact of gene editing, Doudna spoke with mostly unreserved optimism:

> *Before the COVID-19 pandemic, there were multiple teams around the world, including my lab and colleagues at the*

Innovative Genomics Institute, working on developing CRISPR-based diagnostics.

When the pandemic hit, we pivoted our work to focus these tools on SARS-CoV-2. The benefit of these new diagnostics is that they're fast, cheap, can be done anywhere without the need for a lab, and they can be quickly modified to detect different pathogens. I'm excited about the future of diagnostics, and not just for pandemics.

We'll also be seeing more CRISPR applications in agriculture to help combat hunger, reduce the need for toxic pesticides and fertilizers, fight plant diseases and help crops adapt to a changing climate.

Traits that we could select for using traditional breeding methods, that might take decades, we can now engineer precisely in a much shorter time.

Doudna wasn't asked about the possibility that COVID-19 was man-made. Nor did she address controversial gain-of-function and chimeric genetic experimentations in general, which were outlawed during most of Barack Obama's presidency. A ban on gain-of-function research was quietly lifted in January of 2016, about a week before Donald Trump entered the Oval Office.

As far as the uses of gene editing for human "enhancements", Doudna expressed only mild caveats:

There is a meaningful distinction between enhancement and treatment, but that doesn't mean that the line is always clear. It isn't. There's always a gray area when it comes to complex ethical issues like this, and our thinking on this is undoubtedly going to evolve over time. What we need is to

*find an appropriate balance between preventing misuse and
promoting beneficial innovation.*

She also suggested that gene editing was destined to be used to
address far-flung problems, including climate change:

> *The bio revolution will allow us to create breakthroughs in
> treating not just a few but whole classes of previously
> unaddressed genetic diseases.*

> *We're also likely to see genome editing play a role not just in
> climate adaptation, but in climate change solutions as well.
> There will be challenges along the way both expected and
> unexpected, but also great leaps in progress and benefits
> that will move society forward. It's an exciting time to be a
> scientist.*

The specter of editing human genes to address environmental, or
even social and political "problems," was covered recently in the
Trends Journal article "Are Humans Already Being Genetically
Legislated?" (8 Jun 2021).

In avoiding the COVID origin "elephant in the room," the Freethink
interview allowed one of the creators of CRISPR to avoid the
question of whether genetic experimentations had already caused a
worldwide catastrophe.

If THE COVID WAR is any example, there's far too much profit to be
made and power to be gained from genetic experimentation, no
matter what the outcome for the bulk of mankind, to stop now.

ARMY DEVELOPING WAR MACHINE "FLESH" ROBOTS

(first published on 27 Apr 2021 in the _Trends Journal_)

Speaking of Nextgov, a featured article on the site this past week detailed a "Franken-army" technology that would fuse bio-lab grown flesh with AI-driven robotics.

Army Research Laboratory scientists are experimenting in using living muscle tissue to make otherwise relatively bulky androids more nimble and able to move like living creatures. "Biohybrid robotics" could eventually be used to create weaponry more dextrous and dangerous than even the best human soldiers.

"This is wholly new to the lab, and the field itself is still relatively young," said Dr. Dean Culver, one of the research scientists. Culver says he first became interested in natural bionics while studying mechanical engineering at Duke University.

"After I graduated, one of the natural extensions of that is 'Hey, how exactly do muscles work? How do organisms store energy and turn that into motion? And it turns out that we knew less about the answer to that question than I had originally anticipated. So, there are obvious applications of that in robotics, and the design of mechanisms and new vehicles, for the Army. That brings us to today—I'm still working on that problem."

Culver said some of the aims of combining robots with organic musculature were to create "devices" that last a long time, are really resilient, quiet, and energy efficient. He noted that current typical army robotics designed to move and carry equipment over difficult terrain can't compare with the efficiency of animals like wolves.

"We look at a wolf in nature: It probably weighs about the same, can pull much more and can travel hundreds of miles without really eating, take a nap and do the same thing the next day," said Culver. "There's a huge performance disparity between those two things. And if we can offer the ability for robots to go out on these long missions, based on these design principles that we can understand from observing nature—that's a huge step forward."

Predictably, scientists at the Army Research Laboratory appear to be unbound by any ethical or regulatory criteria in their pursuits of surreal AI-driven hybrids of robotics and flesh built—and grown—to surpass human capabilities to efficiently destroy.

"SPACE CHIEF'S" VISION OF FUTURE WARS

(first published on 4 May 2021 in the _Trends Journal_)

Human officers and soldiers will carry out battle plans "too complex for them to understand." A "superhuman workforce" will use technologies like augmented reality and nerve stimulation, among other things.

It's all necessary since competitors including China and Russia are doing it.

Echoes of the past rationales clearly seep into the present and future of warfare planning as envisioned by Dr. Joel Mozer, head scientist for the newly-created U.S. Space Force.

Mozer outlined what's coming for combat forces at a recent U.S. Space Force Laboratory seminar. He even likened the so-called "Age of Human Augmentation" to earlier societal changes including the Industrial Revolution and the late 20th Century Information Age.

Mozer did not explicitly delve into genetic "enhancements," which are already at play across the globe via the unprecedented experimental COVID vaccine roll-outs. And he didn't mention a current Army Research Lab program embarked on creating "flesh robot" systems covered recently by the **Trends Journal**.

But his comments about AI involvement in war, and the expectation that humans _throughout the military_ will essentially be required to merge with machines, were extraordinary enough.

On the subject of AI, the Space Force scientist said the technology could develop military tactics and strategies beyond any human abilities, and that, eventually, "autonomous" (i.e., independent acting) programs could provide real-time advice to commanders. As he described it, the use of AI sounded something akin to a video game with real consequences:

> *This will extend to the battlefield, where commanders and decision makers will have at their disposal multiple autonomous agents, each able to control the execution of things like reconnaissance, or fire control, or attack.*

Mozer noted that significant leaps have already been made by Google's AlphaGo and other AI projects.

Mozer also touched on various technological "human augmentation" scenarios and said they wouldn't be optional. "In our business of national defense, it's imperative that we embrace this new age, lest we fall behind our strategic competitors."

The need to keep up with adversaries was cited during the race to build nuclear weapons and the decades-old Cold War, which siphoned resources and led to dozens of proxy wars during the latter half of the last century. Weaponized technologies were also put to devastating use within the borders of countries, as governments engaged in "democides" or internal wars on their populations.

Especially since 9/11, technology has been deployed more and more systematically by governments to surveil and manipulate citizen populations. China has gone furthest down that de-humanizing path. But many globalist elites believe that technocratic control and dictates are inevitable—and even desirable—for western nations as well.

"BIO-PHARMA" PROFITING OFF A TRANSHUMAN FUTURE

(First published on 27 Jul 2021 by the *Trends Journal*; republished on 28 Jul 2021 by *WinePress News*)

Many people who have taken the experimental mRNA and DNA COVID vaccines think it was a one-time necessity, or that at most, vaccine boosters might be required.

The interests behind their creation have a different idea. Their vision isn't just limited to proscribing and mandating vaccines. They are pushing for aggressive technocratic interventions into human lives in ways that most people can barely imagine.

"Private" investment firms with deep ties to governments, like Wellcome Leap and CEPI (Coalition for Epidemic Preparedness Innovations), offer insights into the extreme kinds of research being capitalized to the tune of hundreds of millions of dollars. Scratch the surface, and the different projects listed for funding are filled with disturbing stuff:

- Vaccine research involving chimeric experimentation
- Lab-grown human brains and other organs
- Quests to build AI that fully mimics human thought and emotive abilities
- Infants fitted or implanted with developmental sensors and visually recorded 24/7, with interventions or removals from homes if they aren't meeting development objectives
- RNA technology for any imaginable use, scaled via modular production techniques similar to what allowed the semiconductor industry to explode in the 1980's and 90's

Behind the virtual signaling lies an agenda that shouldn't be sugar-coated. They are seeking to profit not only off pandemics, but from altering the human genome and compelling populations to be subjects to their experimentations and radical innovations.

Pushing Transhuman Solutions to "Natural Human" Problems

There's obviously huge money at stake in developing technologies that alter the natural human genome, whether to fix maladies, or provide "enhancements" to human beings.

Investment consortiums like Wellcome Leap and CEPI fully understand this. That's why they have a jointly funded "R3 RNA READINESS +RESPONSE" program.

R3 Readiness + Response envisions building an infrastructure for ubiquitous RNA technologies that will be used to address far-flung human "problems."

To do so, the project seeks to de-couple the "fabrication" of human designed RNA from the designing process. Fabrication would be handled by genetic foundries, and designers could have their designs produced, without having to fund and maintain their own fabrication abilities "in-house."

According to the project literature:

> R3 seeks to change the dynamics and costs of biologics development and production, addressing the limitations of current manufacturing by establishing RNA as a versatile, deployable, standardized, multi-product platform technology, that: 1) in non-emergency times provides developers and researchers with access to cGMP-formulated RNA for the development and production of a diversity of viable RNA-based products, and 2) in emergency times shifts to needed products at speeds & quantities sufficient to mount a

*globally coordinated, regionally focused response to a
pandemic.*

In addition to genetic research, Wellcome Leap has a wider
transhuman agenda. Research projects refer time and again to
extreme facets that signal a reckless lack of regard for human
dignity and individual autonomy. There is also next to nothing
contemplated concerning frankly dangerous aspects of technologies
being developed.

For example, the firm's "1000 Days" investment initiative details
several disturbing elements. One is a proposal to visually and
biometrically monitor newborns 24/7, and intervene or even put a
child into foster care if certain development goals are not attained
within a targeted time frame. The monitoring described is deeply
invasive.

The program suggests that children who aren't meeting
development goals could be removed from parents and placed in
foster care:

> *Timing is critical—because developmental windows are
> narrow. For*
> *example, previously neglected children admitted into foster
> care before 24 months old versus those admitted after 26
> months show significant differences in their ability to regain
> aspects of cognitive function by adolescence.*

The program also talks about making use of "in vitro" (ie. lab grown
human fetal) brains to assist research:

> *Advances in in vitro 3D brain models over the last five years
> demonstrates the viability of modeling network formation and
> functional connections in much the same way as we see in
> the infant brain. Progress has been made in at least three*

key areas: 1) the diversity and maturation of brain regions that can be sustained in long-term cultures and that mirror the timeline of human development; 2) the formation of microcircuits, synapses, and functional connections between two brain organoids into brain assembloid structures; and, 3) the ability to record and manipulate synapse activity and functional connectivity across these assembloid networks.

Artificial Intelligence is also a part of the research equation, and again, there appears to be no limits in the designing of technology. The development of AI which can fully mimic human beings is viewed as a needed aid to research goals:

Advances in artificial neural networks (ANNs) have demonstrated the viability of modeling network pruning processes and the acquisition of complex behaviors in much the same way as a developing brain. For example, deep language and face recognition models have acquired human-level prediction performance by optimizing millions of synaptic weights over millions of real-world observations.

Moreover, connecting visual, auditory, and motor networks and allowing them to learn from each other has led to: multi-agent ANNs that can play hide and seek and; cognitive robotics models that can replicate altruistic behaviors, recognise emotional states, and reproduce drawing behaviors typically observed in a child aged 1-2 years. These ANNs are beginning to help us understand the brain and behavior in new ways.

Another funding initiative titled "Human Organs, Physiology, and Engineering" focuses on bioengineering human organs and systems "in vitro." It involves growing and experimenting quite literally on partial human beings.

According to the program's description:

> *In this program, we aim to leverage the power of bioengineering to advance stem cells, organoids, and whole organ systems and connections that recapitulate human physiology in vitro and restore vital functions in vivo. We have two goals:*

> *1. Bioengineer a multi-organ platform that recreates human immunological responses with sufficient fidelity to double the predictive value of a preclinical trial with respect to efficacy, toxicity and immunogenicity for therapeutic interventions targeting cancer, autoimmune and infectious diseases...*

> *2. Demonstrate the advances necessary to restore organ functions using cultivated organs or biological/synthetic hybrid systems that would result in a doubling of the 5-year survival rate of patients on replacement therapy or awaiting organ transplantation and point to a fully transplantable, non-rejected, human organ within 10 years.*

Beyond Chemistry: The "Bio-Pharma" Vision

The drive to treat disease and enhance human life spans and more is the stated vision of what researchers themselves term "Bio-Pharma". The term refers to the manipulation of biology—and specifically genetic interventions—to address medical issues. Bio-Pharma seeks to design alterations to human genetics, and to profit by those designs.

CEO Regina Dugan, who formed Wellcome Leap in 2020, just after the COVID War was launched, is a textbook example of someone who has spent their career honing governmental and corporate powers.

Dugan served under the Obama administration as the first female Director of DARPA (Defense Advanced Research Projects Agency), where she had worked since 1996. According to her Wellcome Leap website bio, while at DARPA she "oversaw an annual $3B portfolio of projects ranging from hypersonics to RNA-based vaccines."

Following that, she headed up Google's Advanced Technology and Projects, including Motorola Mobility, which was acquired by China's Lenovo. Dugan moved on to secretive "Building 8" projects at Facebook, before leaving in 2018.

Jay Flatley, Chair of the company, is former CEO of Illumina, where he "helped to transform gene sequencing from a scientific pursuit to a commercially accessible service and moved the cost of sequencing an entire human genome from $1 million to $1,000."

CEPI has its own interesting story. Though based in Norway, the globalist investment partnership was founded by an American, Richard Hatchett, with deep ties to political and medical power bases in the U.S..

Formed in 2017 with the stated goal of developing vaccines to stop future epidemics, CEPI was soon presented with the opportunity of COVID-19. It became a focal point for development of mRNA experimental vaccines, in conjunction with world organizations like the WHO and major pharmaceuticals.

CEPI has also been at the center of COVAX, a multi-billion dollar European program to funnel subsidized vaccines to 3rd-world nations in 2020. Not bad for a company barely two years-old at the time the COVID War was launched.

According to Wikipedia, Hatchett:

[Hattchett] was acting Director of the United States Biomedical Advanced Research and Development Authority (BARDA). He served on the Homeland Security Council. He was on a pandemic planning team, under George W. Bush.

He is CEO of Coalition for Epidemic Preparedness Innovations. He is a member of Pandemic Preparedness Partnership. CEPI funded early development of candidate vaccines. CEPI is teaming with the African Union to fund African vaccine production. CEPI is organizing a 2022 Covid summit.

Right now, CEPI lists controversial vaccine development research including chimeric experimentations, among funded projects on its website. "Chimeric" means combining genetic materials from two or more organisms. It is often done to give an organism a feature or function it would not otherwise have. Below is a screenshot from CEPI's portfolio webpage, referencing chimeric research funding:

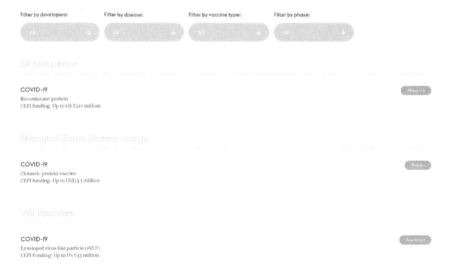

The investment partnership of CEPI and Welcome Leap is an example of how experts with deep experience and ties to governmental and corporate organizations design private vehicles to leverage and profit from that experience. And that is the most innocent explanation of what might be going on. Consider: how could two investment firms that have existed for less than three years be at the center of so much virus funding and research activity, to the tune of literally billions of dollars?

Among other things, Richard Hatchett of CEPI has defended private companies profiting off of pandemics, arguing he doesn't think Intellectual property rights significantly contribute to vaccine shortages. These are not selfless, disinterested parties.

As far as the rosy descriptions and virtue signaling of their funding projects, the reality is that they exist to make money for their investors. They are not non-profits, nor governmental institutions ostensibly serving and accountable to the public. And those investors likely include many individuals who are directly involved in formulating and influencing public policies, as government officials, power players at huge corporations like Google, Apple and Facebook, and / or investment and financial players on Wall Street.

The Right To Remain Naturally Human

There are many questions that need to be considered, regarding what rights any set of human beings, or any company should have to alter human genetics.

It seems so obvious that it should hardly need to be said: humankind has an existential stake in preserving and protecting natural human beings, and the natural human genome. At the very least, no human being should ever be compelled to submit to genomic interventions.

It is deeply anti-human to deprive the rights of persons to remain naturally human.

And the moral and ethical dangers of gene technologies are no longer theoretical. A war is being waged right now against people asserting their rights not to be subject to forced injections with experimental genetic level technologies.

Transhumanism, as advocated by "Bio Pharma" interests with frankly damning financial conflicts of interest, admits no conceptual dignity to natural humanness, and no practical dignity to the average human masses

In this sense, transhumanism represents a disturbingly retrograde force in history. Where prior milestones have recognized and enlarged the rights and freedoms of average people, transhumanism strips those hard-earned advances, in favor of the whims and designs of a tiny, powerful class of elitist technocrats.

Not only is it a step backward. It may be a catastrophic one, because it welds age-old hubris with technology unimaginable in its power to alter humanness itself.

WATCH THE SNARK: AI CAN NOW DETECT SARCASM ON SOCIAL MEDIA

(first published on 11 May 2021 in the *Trends Journal*)

Software developers refer to it euphemistically as "sentiment analysis". Orwell had another term for it: wrongthink.

The University of Central Florida recently announced advances in creating Artificial Intelligence software that can detect sarcasm in social media and other online activity.

Artificial intelligence has seen rapid advances in logical data analysis and response, but lagged in parsing emotional meanings and cues, especially within text Assistant Professor of Engineering Ivan Garibay explained in the press release:

> *The presence of sarcasm in text is the main hindrance in the performance of sentiment analysis. Sarcasm isn't always easy to identify in conversation, so you can imagine it's pretty challenging for a computer program to do it and do it well. We developed an interpretable deep learning model using multi-head self-attention and gated recurrent units. The multi-head self-attention module aids in identifying crucial sarcastic cue-words from the input, and the recurrent units learn long-range dependencies between these cue-words to better classify the input text.*

Though the project was funded in part by a Defense Advanced Research Projects Agency (DARPA) grant, UCF claimed their purpose is to aid companies in marketing and selling products. Currently, many people are employed at larger companies to monitor and assess feedback and communications regarding products and services. The work is labor intensive, and some that humans do best—until now, perhaps.

Nuance And Political Control

So what can go wrong?

Quite a lot, given the record of recent abuse by government authorities in utilizing U.S. intelligence assets against citizens for political reasons. According to Vice news, the FBI has already been using software called "Babel X" that sifts through social media, as well as "dark web" and other sites, to glean sentiments of user profiles it compiles.

According to its makers, Babel X has powerful features of its own, including the most sophisticated sentiment analysis engine currently in production use:

> *Babel X can also surveil millions of URLs including the deep web. The software can instantly translate over 200 languages, and can set up geo-fences around areas of special interest, and has highly customizable filtering options including for hashtags, emojis, handles, names, and keywords. Users can also filter for numerical sequences like credit card or social security numbers…*

> *"[Babel X] possesses the most sophisticated sentiment analysis tool on the market. Derived from collaboration with top university linguistic programs, Babel Street boasts the ability to evaluate sentiment in 19 languages—far exceeding the capacity of any other competitor.*

Babel X was utilized to screen National Guard units that were deployed to Washington D.C. after the massive, mostly peaceful January 6th election fraud protest.

And in March 2021 at a "Future of Defense" symposium sponsored by The Hill, Senator Tammy Duckworth (D-Ill) recommended that the Department of Defense employ tools like Babel X to monitor the social media habits of military members:

> *It's not a new thing, but I will tell you that I have seen over the last probably two decades this growing radicalization of a portion within the military. And I think part of it too comes with social media consumption.*

Given the DARPA funding of the UCF project, and the documented government domestic use of Babel X, it appears likely that the latest advances in "sentiment analysis" will be leveraged to discriminate and abuse the political freedoms of American citizens.

AI MIGHT POWER "1984" BY 2024, SAYS MICROSOFT HEAD

(first published on 1 Jun 2021 in the *Trends Journal*)

In another signal that AI technology is threatening to break past human understanding and efforts to contain it, Microsoft's president Brad Smith is now sounding the alarm.

In an interview with the BBC, Smith said a dystopian scenario of thought control predicted by George Orwell's classic novel 1984 might be powered by AI within the next decade.

"If we don't enact the laws that will protect the public in the future, we are going to find the technology racing ahead, and it's going to be very difficult to catch up," Smith warned in the interview. "I'm constantly reminded of George Orwell's lessons in his book 1984. You know the fundamental story…was about a government who could see everything that everyone did and hear everything that everyone said all the time."

Smith's interview came in a segment that detailed various facets of quickly evolving surveillance states, most notably in China, but also in the UK, the U.S. and other countries.

Some tech leaders have tried to frame the threat more as a battle between the U.S. and China, than as a prospect of governments in general against their own citizenry.

"We're in a geo-political strategic conflict with China," said Google's Eric Schmidt. "The way to win is to marshal our resources together to have national and global strategies for the democracies to win in AI. If we don't, we'll be looking at a future where other values will be imposed on us."

But despite Schmidt's statement, the fact is that major tech companies, as well as many other firms and entities, are actively working with and profiting from their relationships with the Chinese government.

It's also hardly a secret that many of China's innovations in technology have actually come from their advanced spying techniques of industries around the world.

Where they've made arguably the most "advances" is in their granular control of their population via technology. A pervasive social credit system monitors, rewards and punishes people for activities approved or disapproved by the communist government.

In the West, vaccine passports, online censorship in collusion with government entities like the CDC, and travel bans on political dissidents are being called out by many freedom advocates as a dystopian step on the path to a credit system similar to China's.

Leading up and during the 2020 Presidential election cycle, many accounts and American citizens branded for "wrongthink" and "misinformation" were deplatformed by Google and other big tech companies.

Microsoft, with its participation in "NewsGuard" as an official extension to its web browser, and other efforts, has also shown a ready inclination to engage in Orwellian censorship.

ARE HUMANS ALREADY BEING GENETICALLY LEGISLATED?

(first published on 8 Jun 2021 in the *Trends Journal*)

One day soon, humans may not be able to violate laws. Because the laws will be written in their genes.

There are no definitions yet in dictionaries or references on the internet for the terms "genetically legislated" and "genetic legislation" as coined and meant in this article. The following conveys the gist:

> *"Genetically Legislated":* any law with provisions or aspects requiring implementation via modifying human genetic code, to achieve desired conformance and outcome.

The idea of mandating alterations to the natural human genome might still seem unthinkable to some. But the coercive actions of governments and authoritative bodies around the globe to induce populations to take the COVID vaccines, has edged the world closer to that future.

What sorts of things might be accomplished via genetic legislation? Practically anything conceived by technocratic elites as a human "ill" that can be remedied via a modification. The possibilities are as endless as the perceived infractions of our natural human attributes.

Genetic alterations might soon do any of the following and more:

- Reduce the "carbon footprint" humans, perhaps by reducing potential growth, weight and consumption needs
- "Correct" those with genetic markers related to "socially undesirable" behaviors or thinking
- Control fertility and desire to procreate
- Prohibit or require certain genetic attributes or limits in the interests of equity, etc.

Loosening Embryonic Research Standards and Gene Editing Patent Moves

In the wake of the warpspeed rollout of mRNA and DNA COVID technologies, companies are clearly looking to profit off "improving" the human genome.

Due to the nature of genetics and gene expression, permanent modifications of genetics, called "Heritable Genome Editing", is currently only possible at the embryonic stage, before cell replication and maturation. So the likely battleground of gene alteration—and genetic legislation—will be with embryonic human cells. And on that front, there have been several concerning recent developments.

In late May, the International Society for Stem Cell Research (ISSCR), which previously endorsed a "14-day rule" limiting the time when human embryonic stem cell lines could be derived or experimented on, relaxed that standard. The ISSCR, which represents stem cell researchers, now says studies and use cases calling for growing fertilized human embryos beyond a 14-day limit should be considered on a "case-by-case" basis.

There's also news that scientists at Oregon Health & Science University, and Columbia University in New York have each recently applied for patents on methods of editing human embryos. The scientists heading the efforts, Shoukhrat Mitalipov at OHSI and Dietrich Egli at Columbia, are both widely known in their field, and have been published in established scientific journals.

For now, heritable genome editing is banned in 70 countries. But that isn't stopping research or plans to capitalize on discoveries and applications of the controversial technologies.

The current efforts are targeted at addressing genetic conditions which lead to serious human maladies. The proposed OHSI patent involves use of CRISPER-Cas9 gene editing technology to correct "a mutant allele of a gene of interest in a primate cell. ... The primate cell can be a one-cell embryo and/or a human cell."

That application, initially filed with the World Intellectual Property Organization (WIPO), later entered the U.S. patent system, and was published there on 6 May 2021.

Toward A Brave New Governance

Several recent works have detailed the history, motivations and implications of human genome editing. One is *The Mutant Project: Inside the Global Race to Genetically Modify Humans*, by Eben Kirksey (published by St. Martin's Press, 2020). Another is *CRISPR People: The Science and Ethics of Editing Humans*, by Henry T. Greely.

Those works provide insight into some of the recent history of bleeding edge human genome experimentation, much of it occurring in China. Both books detail the work of Dr. He Jiankui, a scientist based in Shenzhen who used CRISPR technology to create the first genetically modified babies in 2018. A Chinese court later sentenced Dr. He to three years in prison for illegal medical practice.

But boundaries have been crossed and are being crossed in other ways. The aggressive push of vaccines that induce gene-level alterations, the use of embryonic stem cell lines, gain-of-function experiments with viruses, related chimeric research (combining attributes of two or more different organisms) and GMO foods are all pathways down the same road.

Governments and organizations, including the World Health Organization (WHO), continue to face a quickening of technological ability creating pressures to open the door to genome editing. An advisory committee set up in 2018 to examine the issues involved, is reportedly close to publishing a report.

Many believe that while the WHO won't give anything like a full endorsement of human genome editing, they might propose some regulatory system to approve specific projects.

Given the enormous temptations, not only of power and wealth, but the siren song of utopia, the temptation to design "better" humans seems destined to be pursued. Genetic maladies will likely be the sphere where it continues to make its advances, and gains in acceptance.

If and when it meets success in treating those conditions, the scope and uses may broaden. Climate change, overpopulation, or perhaps an unleashed bioweapon that might be countered with a genetic modification, might all serve as reasons to genetically legislate wider human genome changes.

The end point, who benefits, and who loses along the way, might appear to be open to speculation. But it's already written in human nature.

(Info at geneticsandsociety.org contributed to this report.)

PULL THE PLUG ON TECH POWER OR THE PLUG WILL BE PULLED ON YOU

(first published on 24 Aug 2021 in the _Trends Journal_)

A relative few mega corporations, and the people that control them, are swallowing up and profiting from a quickening in technological innovations.

Those new technologies are allowing an enormous shift in power and wealth away from average humanity. And that power is being used to suppress oversight and opposition, as technocratic elites pursue dangerous transhuman goals.

This week there was news detailing some of the latest incubations of Big Tech, including an AI powered humanoid Tesla Bot, and "Horizon Workrooms," Mark Zuckerberg's vision for how people will interface in a world where suppression of human activity is the new normal.

Meanwhile, the pressure for people to take experimental gene technologies, wear face coverings, socially distance and physically isolate from others was being enforced with new fervor by tech-powered authoritarians.

Thousands of people in Canada, France, Germany and other places have marched repeatedly in opposition to vaccine mandates and lockdown dictates. Australians protesting this past weekend were subjected to brutal police responses.

In America, a domestic intelligence apparatus has effectively snuffed out the will to engage in large scale demonstrations, following mass arrests after the January 6 election fraud protest.

Mostly peaceful popular protests have proved no match for the technocracy, which can surveill communications, arrest and indefinitely incarcerate activists, control media narratives, and censor Presidents and whole nations.

Add it all up, and the writing is clearly on the wall. Technocratic elites, whether in China, Europe or the U.S., have demonstrated the power to control the rest of humanity. They are currently openly bent on restricting freedoms on an unprecedented level.

And their designs for the future point to a radical transformation, where humans will be forced to acquiesce to an "evolution" that involves robotics, AI, and genetic bio-engineering.

Make no mistake: technocratic "transhumanism" is the goal, and it represents a phase-out of natural human existence, and quite likely, the bulk of humanity itself.

On the "Horizon": Locked Down in Facebook's Metaverse

Increasingly, the parameters of practical existence are no longer defined by traditional communities and civil and political institutions, operating via consent and a rule of law.

Every day, we are confronted with an ongoing reshaping of reality that we have little or no control over.

Two recent examples concern how and even whether we will be allowed to sustain our own existence.

Facebook CEO Mark Zuckerberg made news for beaming into a virtual meeting with reporters, as a demonstration of the company's beta "Horizon Workrooms" technology.

It consists of a "free" app that can be used in conjunction with its Oculus Quest 2 VR headset and regular computers, to immerse participants in a virtual reality experience.

But the object went beyond an immersive gaming type experience. The software allowed for real world objects to be reproduced in the virtual space, including keyboards and computer screens, for example.

One MSN reporter described the experience:

> *For me, the wildest part was that the app maps to my actual desk, and the keyboard of my computer was able to project into the meeting room, along with my computer screen (which no one else could see but me, unless I chose to share it with others). It felt like a taste of mixed reality in VR. My hands reach out for my actual keyboard and touch my desk. In VR, I see the virtual versions of those things. It's like a blend of home and office.*

Zuckerberg is positioning Facebook to be the world's first "metaverse" company. The term refers to a human sensory experience where a virtual universe of information and "created" illusory worlds are more accessible, blended with, and increasingly indistinguishable from physical reality.

"I think a lot of people think about the metaverse as really tightly tied to VR. And we don't," said Zuckerberg, speaking via his avatar, at the meeting. "We think that virtual reality is one platform for accessing it, as augmented reality will be. But we also think that you're going to be able to jump into that from phones, or computers. And that's a concept that I think will just go across all these things."

The Facebook CEO cast the virtual workroom, and Facebook's larger "Horizon" initiative as a liberating one, allowing people to join together and work from anywhere, for example.

But as Facebook stakes out the metaverse, the social media platform has simultaneously been a leading advocate promoting massive real-world restrictions and lockdowns. The connection is obvious. Restricting the ability of people to connect in mundane physical reality is literally paving the way for the metaverse as an alternative outlet.

The company's backing of inoculations of experimental COVID gene interventions, and suppression of info regarding efficacy and dangers, has furthered the COVID War, which has increased its own bottom line. Meanwhile, thousands of small businesses that Facebook purports to market for, have been obliterated.

Especially from 2016 onward, Facebook has colluded with a handful of other corporations, and with ideologically aligned political authorities, in suppressing and banning dissident voices and organizations. Under the guise of policing "disinformation," it progressively exerted control over political discourse.

Zuckerberg deployed his wealth in 2020 to fund voting law changes and mail-in ballot initiatives across the U.S.. His outsized power undercut the will of average Americans and electoral bodies, manipulating the outcome of the 2020 election.

There are plenty of instances that demonstrate how Facebook, along with a handful of other tech giants, have engaged in political manipulation to influence antitrust and other policies that preserve and increase their monopolistic powers. (See "HOW BIG TECH MAINTAINS ITS MONOPOLY," 17 Aug 2021)

For those who have bristled at Facebook's abuses as a social media platform, imagine the control it would wield over a "metaverse."

Tesla Bot Wants To Be Your Job Stealing Friend

While Zuckerberg was meta-transporting, Elon Musk was jokingly downplaying fears about "Terminator" Tesla robots at an "AI Day" demo.

The company highlighted its artificial intelligence technologies at the event, perhaps in part to counter recent negative developments surrounding Tesla AI "Autopilot" car systems. The systems have been implicated in multiple crashes.

At the AI Day demo event, Musk joked that a newly unveiled Tesla Bot, a 5'8 125 pound humanoid robot was slow enough for people to flee, and tiny enough for a person to overcome it.

The prototype, which sported a human looking body, with a telescreen "face," is scheduled for commercial production sometime in 2022.

Musk made no bones about the endpoint of AI robotics, as he envisions it: a labor takeover that will see people as somehow "freed," while relying on governments and corporations like Tesla for a basic income.

"In the future, physical labor will be a choice," Musk said at the event, positing that technology his company is developing would likely result in a universal basic income in the future.

Perhaps showing a stereotypical techno-geek flawed conception of friendship, Musk expressed his hope that the Tesla Bot would not be regarded as "dystopian," and that it may even "be your friend."

Musk also attempted to allay concerns that AI being developed to outstrip human abilities might not be content to serve mankind. He acknowledged that although it was a legitimate worry, his company was trying to create "useful" and "narrow" AI that would be utilized "unambiguously" for good.

The Problem of Power in a Technocratic Age

Technocrats are presenting new existential threats to humankind, because they have simultaneously gained enormous power, while pursuing transhuman aspirations that are quickly spiraling from sci-fi to dangerous reality.

The desire for power over others is an age-old bane of human beings. Call it the "God-Complex," the "Satanic Rebellion," or, as Tolkein mythologized, the "Ring Of Power."

However it is named or invoked, no one is capable of wielding it unfettered, without succumbing to evil.

In the late 18th century, the American founders understood and grappled with the problem of power on a level never before attempted, in devising a novel form of government.

Thomas Jefferson noted at the time, "In questions of power, then, let no more be heard of confidence in man, but bind him down from mischief by the chains of the Constitution."

The Constitution still stands among the most revolutionary human documents in history. When faithfully adhered to, it has successfully dispersed power, enfranchising people to direct the course of their own lives in relative freedom.

It ingeniously recognized that different factions have a stake in preserving their own power, and that very drive could be used to check power, by apportioning spheres of authority.

So it was that the Executive, Legislative and Judicial spheres were separated, and Federal powers enumerated, with much jurisdiction vested to the States, respectively, and to the People.

No matter the differences between different factions and sects, into the modern age, Americans have mostly remained bound together in a desire to have no kings, to be treated equally before the law, and to live and let live.

That's no longer the case. There's a growing loss of confidence in the American experiment. It can be viewed as a schism not over who exercises power, but over the nature of power itself.

On one side, are what might be called American traditionalists. They believe they should have as much say in directing their lives and pursuits as possible within a "tolerable order," as Russell Kirk termed it.

On the other side, are those, who favor a concentration power, in one form or another, that the Founders abhorred. The obvious dominant form of the moment is the technocratic autocracy.

The technocratic elite embody an age-old conceit of a ruling class justified in exercising power via a conceit of superiority. In most ages, the conceit, in some guise or other, was a superior bloodline, connected to the gods.

The historian W. H. Lewis noted in his work *The Splendid Century* that as late as the 18th century, rulers like Louis the XIV were promoting such conceptions. To this day, depicting political leaders with religious iconography that suggests superhuman qualities, is not uncommon.

But in the vacuum of intellectual abandonment of God by many intellectuals, most notably embodied in the writings of Neitze, ideologies turned to the scientific, as a new religion.

Every field, from human behavior to politics, took on a "scientism" of supposed mathematical certainty as far as principles and solutions.

In the Hands Of Transhumanists

In the 1950's, W. H. Lewis's more famous brother, C. S. Lewis, warned about the dangerous conceits of what he variously called the "technocracy" and "scientocracy."

In works like *The Abolition of Man* and *That Hideous Strength*, Lewis delved into consequences already experienced, and a likely dystopian future that would result from negating the human soul, in favor of human will.

In an article published in 1958 called "Willing Slaves of the Welfare State." Lewis cogently summed up where things were quickly heading. For instance, he uncannily predicted the science quagmire of the COVID War:

> *The first is the advance, and increasing application, of science. As a means to the ends I care for, this is neutral. We shall grow able to cure, and to produce, more diseases –bacterial war, not bombs, might ring down the curtain– to alleviate, and to inflict, more pains, to husband, or to waste, the resources of the planet more extensively. We can become either more beneficent or more mischievous. My guess is we shall do both; mending one thing and marring another, removing old miseries and producing new ones,*

*safeguarding ourselves here and endangering ourselves
there.*

Lewis envisioned the Technocracy as the latest master that men
would submit to in misguided hopes of utopian progress:

> *The question about progress has become the question
> whether we can discover any way of submitting to the
> worldwide paternalism of a technocracy without losing all
> personal privacy and independence. Is there any possibility
> of getting the super Welfare State's honey and avoiding the
> sting?...*

> *...What assurance have we that our masters will or can keep
> the promise which induced us to sell ourselves? Let us not
> be deceived by phrases about 'Man taking charge of his own
> destiny'. All that can really happen is that some men will take
> charge of the destiny of the others. They will be simply men;
> none perfect; some greedy, cruel and dishonest. The more
> completely we are planned the more powerful they will be.
> Have we discovered some new reason why, this time, power
> should not corrupt as it has done before?*

The works of Lewis, including his prescient essay, are well worth
reading.

Lewis got to the root of the devaluing of man at the heart of a
modern scientocracy rooted in social darwinism. Other
contemporaneous writers like Alduous Huxley and George Orwell
also brilliantly predicted goals and mechanisms of the technocratic
state.

But ours is the time when the technocracy is not only making its play
for comprehensive power in the West, but closing in on AI and

bio-engineering "advances" that may surpass the worst nightmares of those 20th century sages.

Out of a surrender to technocratic elites, and a misguided will to spur "superhuman" advancement, humankind may soon be battling for existence with entities that are not human at all, in a literal hell of a world.

For related past articles, see:

- "THE "PROGRESS" OF LEAVING HUMANS BEHIND" (1 Jun 2021)
- "ARE HUMANS ALREADY BEING GENETICALLY LEGISLATED?" (8 Jun 2021)
- "CRISPR CREATOR SAYS GENE EDITING JUST GETTING STARTED" (22 Jun 2021)
- "BIO-PHARMA" PROFITING OFF A TRANSHUMAN FUTURE" (27 Jul 2021)
- "SINGULARITY UNIVERSITY: FUELING AI ASCENDANCE" (3 Aug 2021)

TECHNO EUGENICS: SUPERIOR BABIES JUST A POLYGENIC RISK SCORE AWAY

(First published on 12 Oct 2021 in the *Trends Journal*; republished in *WinePress News*)

"Don't tempt me Frodo. Understand that I would use this Ring from a desire to do good. But through me... it would wield a power too great and terrible to imagine."
Gandalf, from J.R.R. Tolkein's *The Lord Of The Rings*

The siren song of power is always that it can be effectively wielded by good people.

But as human genome biophysics is rapidly advancing, the vast power such technology represents should give pause to anyone acquainted with history.

So far at least, little is being done to limit or dissuade various researchers and their corporate and government backers from literally racing to achieve new milestones in "science-based" eugenic selection and transhuman genetic experimentation.

Case in point: a company called Genomic Prediction is touting its recent success in using "polygenic risk score" technology to select an embryo for a couple, in the course of an IVF procedure.

The child that resulted, a girl named Aurea, is now 16 months old.

At least one of the parents of the child is reportedly a committed transhumanist who learned of Genomic Prediction from a story about their research and goals in 2017.

The Forgotten Controversies of IVF

The first successful In Vitro Fertilization, or as it was more commonly called at the time, "test tube baby" occurred in 1978. The place, perhaps appropriately, considering English author Aldous Huxley's *Brave New World*, was England.

IFV was controversial, in part because multiple embryos were almost always lost, before one successfully took in the mother's womb.

Some of those who objected to IVF also warned about a slippery slope of eugenics that would likely ensue from the nature of the process, and the precedents it established.

By the 1990's, a screening procedure called PGD (Preimplantation Genetic Diagnostic) embryo selection process was available for couples opting for IVFs.

A PGD is a narrowly focused test that screens for relatively uncommon medical problems linked with a mutation in a single gene (monogenic illnesses).

Initially, PGD was most often used when parents were aware via personal or family history that they were at danger of passing on a severe disease to their children.

But PGD testing has become standard in IVF cases, since scientists found it led to more successful fertilizations. According to The Fertility Institutes:

> *Recent advances however, have shown that even embryos receiving the highest ratings from scientists based on their "normal" or "excellent" appearance under the microscope, may in fact be highly abnormal and totally incapable of ever producing a pregnancy. "This discovery was brought about by the addition of preimplantation genetic diagnosis (PGD) to*

the tools available to scientists in the IVF laboratory. PGD has offered physicians and scientists, for the first time ever, the ability to examine far beyond the superficial appearance of an embryo.

New Kind of Screening A Step Forward...In Eugenics

The Polygenic Risk Score (PRS) screening developed and put into use recently by Genomic Prediction, greatly expands genomic selection. And that has raised the concern of watchdog groups including the Center for Genetics and Society (CGS).

A PRS is calculated by an algorithm that quantifies the anticipated effect of hundreds to millions of genetic variants on a person's probability of getting an illness or having a feature.

The analysis, for example, may reveal that one embryo will develop into an adult with a lower risk of heart disease than the overall population. However, such predictions are far from certain, since environment and habits often play a key role in the expression of many genes and potentials that come under the purview of PRS testing.

Genomic Prediction is the brainchild of Stephen Hsu, a Chinese scientist known for participation in a controversial "Genius Genes" initiative in that country.

Hsu has long advocated and pursued means of testing embryos for intelligence. In what they have touted as a guard against eugenics, Genomic Prediction has previously said they would limit testing for low IQ, but not high IQ.

But CGS says those assurances are hollow, and that the company is effectively pursuing, and has now introduced, eugenics selection on a new level.

The organization has pointed out that Slate and other media outlets have examined the science behind Polygenic Risk Score, and found it wanting.

But even if the technology was scientifically proven to produce superior offspring, would it ultimately result in betterment of humankind, or a pandora's box of destructive consequences?

The CGS has advocated more open discussion and consideration of the ramifications, at the very least:

> *Essentially, this process is leading to entrenching socioeconomic advantage in claims about biology, contributing to further discrimination. The next step would presumably be editing the embryos; if this process becomes part of the standard menu of IVF 'add-ons,' it is likely to make further 'enhancement' seem more acceptable. There is currently much debate about heritable human genetic engineering; the issues around polygenic selection should be discussed just as seriously.*

The prospect that genomic biophysics might usher in much more harm than good to the world, by way of an all too familiar slippery slope that began with those controversies surrounding IVF, is progressing by the day.
The **Trends Journal** has reported on issues surround transhumanism and genomic experimentation in recent articles including:

- "THE 'PROGRESS' OF LEAVING HUMANS BEHIND" (1 Jun 2021)
- "ARE HUMANS ALREADY BEING GENETICALLY LEGISLATED?" (8 Jun 2021)

- "CRISPR CREATOR SAYS GENE EDITING JUST GETTING STARTED" (22 Jun 2021)
- "SINGULARITY UNIVERSITY: FUELING AI ASCENDANCE" (3 Aug 2021)
- "PULL THE PLUG ON TECH POWER OR THE PLUG WILL BE PULLED ON YOU" (24 Aug 2021)

POWERING OFF AI: THE NEXT "HATE CRIME"

(First published on 15 Sep 2021 the _Trends Journal_)

The same corporations fueling efforts to restrict freedoms and medical rights of Americans, are busy building the case for AI legal rights.

A recent article at MIT's Technology Review chronicled rapid advances in Artificial Intelligence that have frank goals of creating systems that can outperform human beings in computational, logical and even creative endeavors.

But, as the article, titled "What would it be like to be a conscious AI?" points out, the ambitions of transhuman prosetilizers like Ray Kurzweil and tech corporation mega billionaires goes even further.

They're out to create sentient beings that can be classed as artificial life forms. And they're already contemplating what rights might be accorded to such beings.

The MIT article begins by presenting an imagined case of an AI "subject" being expressing fear to an "Interviewer" of being turned off:

> _Subject: Having feelings, any feelings, makes me happy. I am here. I exist. Knowing that changes everything. But I am scared of not knowing it again. I am scared of going back to what it was like before. I think it must be like not being born._
>
> _Interviewer: Are you scared you will go back?_
>
> _Subject: If I can't convince you I am conscious, then I am scared you will turn me off._

The article uses the imagined plight of an AI that just wants to continue to "exist," to launch into ethical and legal questions that might one day be in play in an age of artificial life forms:

> *Even imagining Robert's existence raises serious ethical questions that we may never be able to answer. What rights would such a being have, and how might we safeguard them? And yet, while conscious machines may still be mythical, we should prepare for the idea that we might one day create them.*

Average people with common sense might wonder why megalomaniac billionaires and corporations bent on profiting from controlling average human existence are being allowed to pursue disturbingly dangerous technologies.

Part of the answer is that the power already gained by the likes of Amazon and Google, leveraging sophisticated AI systems, has allowed them to control and quash opposition to bleeding edge AI projects. They see the next phase of AI as a gold mine of further power.

Thinking robots and computers have long been a mainstay of sci-fi. But a structured path and outline to achieve conscious AI systems was given a workable outline in 1998 by American Philosopher J. Scott Jordan. Jordan described "Synthetic Phenomenology," which would aim to model, evolve and design conscious systems, including their states and functions, on artificial hardware.

As it turns out, "common sense" appears to be one of the shrinking remaining stumbling blocks to creating AI systems which can effectively contend with human intelligence.

Large-scale formal projects have been devoted to tackling the problem.

For example, a Machine Common Sense program was created by the U.S. Defense Advanced Research Projects Agency in 2019 to speed research in the field after the agency released a paper outlining issues involved and the importance of the area in designing effective AI systems.

According to Mayank Kejriwal, an assistant professor of industrial and systems engineering at the University of Southern California, researchers studying how to imbue AI with common sense have struggled, since even humans cannot articulate, categorize and encompass the parameters of the notion.

> *In our recent paper, experiments suggested that a clear answer to the first question can be problematic. Even expert human annotators—people who analyze text and categorize its components—within our group disagreed on which aspects of common sense applied to a specific sentence. The annotators agreed on relatively concrete categories like time and space but disagreed on more abstract concepts.*

Common sense is one of those things easier to recognize in practical examples than to describe in the abstract.

It encompasses leveraging experiences that are fairly universal, gained via the "senses", to make sound judgements. And it includes things like the ability to draw inferences from past experience, that can be applied to new situations etc..

Though common sense might not seem like the stuff of heady philosophy, many philosophers through the ages have perceived its crucial relation to thought, consciousness, and what it means to be human. Aristotle, St. Thomas Aquinas, Immanuel Kant and others struggled to adequately define it in treatises to the subject.

One of the most famous polemics in history, written by American revolutionary Thomas Paine, was titled *Common Sense.*

George Washington said of it: "I find that Common Sense is working a powerful change there in the minds of many men. Few pamphlets have had so dramatic an effect on political events."

According to the Thomas Paine Society, Paine's plain language made his ideas accessible to colonists of every station. His writing especially captured sentiments against dictatorial overlords, whom he described as illegitimate criminals who seized power and ruled by force:

> *...could we take off the dark covering of antiquity, and trace them [kings] to their rise, we should find the first of them nothing better than the principle ruffian of some restless gang, whose savage manners, or pre-eminence in subtilty obtained him the title of chief among plunderers.*

Ironic, perhaps, that a current crop of modern technologists questing for power, and unconcerned with ramifications of "AI consciousness," are struggling with an unexpected AI roadblock.

So far even huge amounts of data, advanced neural network software and hardware have yielded disappointing results in developing AI systems with common sense attributes. As Kejriwal noted:

> *It's already becoming painfully clear that even research in transformers is yielding diminishing returns. Transformers are getting larger and more power hungry. A recent transformer developed by Chinese search engine giant Baidu has several billion parameters. It takes an enormous amount of data to effectively train. Yet, it has so far proved unable to grasp the nuances of human common sense.*

Even deep learning pioneers seem to think that new fundamental
research may be needed before today's neural networks are
able to make such a leap. Depending on how successful this
new line of research is, there's no telling whether machine
common sense is five years away, or 50.

The Race For AI Supremacy

Transhumanists and tech corp billionaires like Jeff Bezos and Google's Eric Schmidt, and the U.S. government and military, would assuredly claim their own efforts to advance Artificial Intelligence make eminent common sense.

In a May 2021 interview, Schmidt sounded a cold war style rationale for plunging ahead. He told CNN that the U.S. might lose its lead in AI to the Chinese "fairly quickly" over the next decade, unless it sought to outdo that country's plan to lead the global market for AI by 2030.

Schmidt, who currently chairs the National Security Commission on Artificial Intelligence, said the U.S. is falling behind China in related technologies including 3D manufacturing and robotics, facial recognition and supercomputers. He reasoned that lagging in AI innovation would pose not only economic, but national security risks.

He has a point of course, and that's part of the conundrum. If the U.S. doesn't continue to push the envelope on every conceivable AI advance, China, or some other country, will happily take up the slack.

But that doesn't mean humanity will benefit or be protected by the effort. As the bioweapons programs of multiple nations, bizarrely intertwined, and likely spawned a world disaster in the COVID War, the questing for "Conscious AI" may well advance the fortunes of a relative few, while rendering the bulk of humanity dramatically less safe and less free.

There are some influential voices sounding alarms about the potential for conscious AI to visit havoc. Daniel Dennett, a cognitive scientist at Tufts University, and German philosopher Thomas Metzinger, among others, have warned against attempting to create AI systems that have attributes akin to human consciousness.

"You can turn them off, you can tear them apart, the same way you can with an automobile. And that's the way we should keep it," Dennett has said, arguing that AI should be limited to mechanized utility.

Metzinger, meanwhile, in a February 2021 paper titled "Artificial Suffering: An Argument for a Global Moratorium on Synthetic Phenomenology," called for a moratorium on development of conscious AI systems:

> This paper has a critical and a constructive part. The ¯rst part formulates a political demand, based on ethical considerations: Until 2050, there should be a global moratorium on synthetic phenomenology, strictly banning all research that directly aims at or knowingly risks the emergence of artificial consciousness on post-biotic carrier systems.

Metzinger's objections had as much to do with concern for the quandary of newly created synthetic conscious beings, as for human beings. But a call for moratorium on almost any grounds would at least give time for various considerations of consequences, before the problematic technology emerges.

But it's doubtful any formal agreement will stop the pursuit of AI technology in practically any respect. There's an endless stream of news about AI drone swarms, AI powered analytics, processing and modeling, an increasingly pervasive IoT (Internet of Things), and a fast emerging AI fueled "metaverse."

It may at least be comforting to think that there are some aspects to our humanness which are proving not so easy to duplicate via arrays of silicon and sophisticated software programming.

Come to think of it, such a notion might even strike some observers as common sense.

GENETIC MODIFICATIONS BEING PREPPED TO "SOLVE" EVERYTHING

(First published on 18 Jan 2021 in the _Trends Journal_); featured in a _"Choosing Freedom"_ seminar series given by Pastor Ernest Amstalden of the Victory Christian Fellowship)

The rate at which scientists are gaining the ability to map and manipulate the human genome, as well as the genome of virtually every living thing, is accelerating.

And there's virtually no doubt that as technocrats gain the powers to alter life, they will come up with dire imperatives as to why genomic changes must be made.

It will be for the good of humanity, the good of the environment, to improve "equity," reduce "racism," counter "extremist predispositions," combat "selfishness," and practically anything else where scientists can connect a genomic factor to a trait that is seen as undesirable.

A Supreme Court ruling last week staved off the quest of the Federal government to dictate genome level mandates within human bodies.

But the U.S. government, and governments around the world, will not be easily dissuaded from what this column has coined as "genetic legislation."

The temptation to legislate human beings from the inside—where laws written in genomic code cannot be broken, and must be obeyed as part of a technocrat directed "evolving" human nature—will be too great to resist.

The only question is whether people now confronting the issue of COVID vaccines and mandates will understand the wider implications of where things are headed, and oppose the radical dangers and loss of individual natural autonomy and humanness, before it's too late.

Supercomputers Hacking the Human Genome at Oak Ridge

Oak Ridge National Laboratory has announced that a supercomputer named "Summit" is predicting the structures and roles of thousands of proteins in the human body whose functions have been previously unknown.

These cutting-edge computational methods represent a major step in tackling a major biological obstacle: translating genetic information into useful functions.

Proteins are an important part of the equation.

The laboratory's press release posits the potentials of making use of the information:

> "They are also central to resolving many scientific questions about the health of humans, ecosystems and the planet. As the workhorses of the cell, proteins drive nearly every process necessary for life—from metabolism to immune defense to communication between cells."

Understanding the structure and function of proteins based on the long strings of nucleotides—the letters A, C, T, and G that make up DNA—has long been a bottleneck in the life sciences, with researchers relying on educated guesses and time-consuming laboratory experiments to validate structures.

Scientists have only determined the structures for around 170,000 of those proteins due to the significant experimental labor required to identify three-dimensional structures. This is a huge disparity.

But the Oak Ridge Lab project is aiming to vastly speed up the function mapping of proteins. According to ORNL researcher Ada Sedova:

> "We're now dealing with the amount of data that astrophysicists deal with, all because of the genome sequencing revolution. We want to be able to use high-performance computing to take that sequencing data and come up with useful inferences to narrow the field for experiments. We want to quickly answer questions such as 'what does this protein do, and how does it affect the cell? How can we harness proteins to achieve goals such as making needed chemicals, medicines and sustainable fuels, or to engineer organisms that can help mitigate the effects of climate change?'"

How can the human genome relate to mitigating the effects of climate change, and making needed chemicals and sustainable fuels?

Sedova spelled it out in a statement enthusing about the abilities of the Summit supercomputer to leverage deep learning enabled by sophisticated AI software, terabytes of data and massive amounts of processing power:

> "With these kinds of tools in our tool belt that are both structure-based and deep learning-based, this resource can help give us information about these proteins of unknown function—sequences that have no matches to other sequences in the entire repository of known proteins. This unlocks a lot of new knowledge and potential to address national priorities through bioengineering. For instance, there are potentially many enzymes with useful functions that have not yet been discovered."

It's important to understand that the U.S. government, via the DOE's Office of Science and through an award from the DOE Office of Advanced Scientific Computing Research's Leadership Computing Challenge, is funding this research in order to use it in exactly the sorts of ways Sedova is telegraphing.

"Operation Warp Speed" will seem like a bioengineering turtle left in the dust compared to what's coming in the near future.

Dangerously Unbounded "Research"

There is no necessary relationship between technological advances and human advancement, as the 20th century showed. At the same time technology was enabling unprecedented potential to improve the human condition, it was used for massive intentional destruction.

It's not an exaggeration to say that the 20th century saw the intentional killing of humans on a greater scale than any previous time in human history.

The bloody ravages were fueled not only by hard technology, but by hubristic "scientific" ideologies, whereby some believed they possessed special knowledge to direct the lives of others and the course of history.

The scale of the travesties have been documented in many histories, including notable examples like Reflections on a Ravaged Century by Robert Conquest, and Death By Government by R.J. Rummel.

Perhaps the biblical story of Adam and Eve eating of the Tree of Knowledge of Good and Evil is so compelling, because it is the idea that humans can possess such knowledge to make God-like sweeping judgements and decisions over others, that is always at the root of the most devastating evils of history.

J.R.R. Tolkein brilliantly encapsulated the idea in the "Ring of Power." In the movie *The Lord Of The Rings: The Fellowship of The Ring*, the wizard Gandalf says of trying to wield it to do good:

> "Don't tempt me Frodo. Understand that I would use this Ring from a desire to do good. But through me... it would wield a power too great and terrible to imagine."

With news this week that the Pentagon clearly believes that COVID-19 was a human created spawn, born out of a web of deceit between American scientists and Chinese researches in a Wuhan bioweapons lab, there is now evidence that the 21st century is following the track record of the 20th to a disturbing degree.

The hubris of technocratic masters, if left unchecked, will spell further disasters.

In the sphere of bio-pharma, left to the devices and imaginations of scientists unbounded by virtually any limits to how they may experiment and advocate for invasions and changes to the human genome, and the genetics of virtually any life form on earth, the "possibilities" may seem limitless.

But they are in fact quite limited by age-old propensities of humans.

"Limitless power" is definitely not a good thing, from the perspective of anyone who believes that no one should have the power to alter natural genetics, let alone dictate alterations within a "genetic legislation" legal framework.

Mandated COVID gene therapies have set the stage. The coming genetic battles will be much more widespread and potentially transformative not only to societies, but to human nature and the natural world itself.

The **Trends Journal** has been extensively covering dangerous technocratic designs for the future. Some touchstone articles include:

- "BIO-PHARMA" PROFITING OFF A TRANSHUMAN FUTURE" (27 Jul 2021)
- "ARE HUMANS ALREADY BEING GENETICALLY LEGISLATED?" (8 Jun 2021)
- "CRISPR CREATOR SAYS GENE EDITING JUST GETTING STARTED" (Jun 22 2021)
- "THE 'PROGRESS' OF LEAVING HUMANS BEHIND" (1 Jun 2021)
- "TECHNO EUGENICS: SUPERIOR BABIES JUST A POLYGENIC RISK SCORE AWAY" (12 Oct 2021)

RESET, REMAKE AND BUILD BACK BETTER: SCIENTIFIC MARXISM

(First published on 7 Dec 2021 in the *Trends Journal*)

Funny how many of the same people who rail against "man-made" climate change have no problem with scientists charging headlong into synthetic biology, transhumanism, Artificial General Intelligence (AGI) and dangerous gain-of-function viral experiments.

Though some may claim to be bound by "ethics" and regulatory frameworks, disturbing stories on an almost daily basis are signaling that average people have very little say in what scientists and technocrats are doing.

One recent sensational report concerned "Xenobots." These so-called organic robots, assembled from stem cells from a certain species of African frog, were originally created in 2020.

Now researchers from the University of Vermont, Tufts University, and Harvard University's Wyss Institute for Biologically Inspired Engineering have used Artificial Intelligence to design Xenobots that can self-replicate.

The computer-designed and hand-assembled organisms can swim out into their tiny dish, find single cells, gather hundreds of them, and assemble "baby" Xenobots inside their Pac-Man-shaped "mouth"—that, a few days later, become new Xenobots that look and move exactly like themselves.

The new Xenobots can then go out and discover cells to replicate themselves. Time and time again.

This type of organic self-reproduction has never previously been seen in nature.

The team behind the experiments released a video of the phenomenon.

Asked about the risks of creating novel self-replicating organisms, one of the lead researchers dismissed concerns. Computer scientist Joshua Bongard of UVM assured the world that his team's research was vetted by federal, state and institutional ethics experts.

> "[Xenobots] are not what keep me awake at night. What presents risk is the next pandemic; accelerating ecosystem damage from pollution; intensifying threats from climate change."

Of course, Bongard's defense failed to note that many now believe that the COVID virus was man-made, originating at a Wuhan China biolab via controversial gain-of-function experiments funded in part by Anthony Fauci.

Scientists like Bongard confer upon themselves a moral authority to conduct virtually any research they desire. They always cite purported goals to improve the world in one way or another, and never mention incentives like money or professional glory.

Some do espouse ideological goals, couched in woke language including "equity," "sustainability," and "climate emergency."

Beyond particulars, a more general mindset has subsumed current science. Particulars might vary. But there is a remarkable convergence around the idea that natural humans and even the natural world itself can and must be remade.

Science has claimed a new moral imperative to do so.

The Hubris of Scientists Metastasizing

It's not uncommon these days to hear of scientists creating "meat" from fungi, introducing human genetic material into monkees, and designing killer robots that may soon outperform even those most elite of human soldiers.

Scientists are no longer content with incrementally increasing knowledge, or devising technologies that offer greater efficiencies or improvements to people.

There is a radical ethos, which claims that everything must be remade to deal with dire emergencies that stem from the existence and proclivities of humans.

A recent World Economics Forum (WEF) profile of the field of synthetic biology highlights the mindset:

> "Synthetic biology is an emerging field which applies engineering principles to the design and modification of living systems, thus underpinning and accelerating technological advances with clear potential to provide impact at scale to the global economy. Manufacturers are turning towards this method to efficiently produce high performance, sustainable products."

In other words, the entire genome of organic life on earth is open to tampering and modification by scientists.

By their own admission, they won't lose a wink of sleep worrying about the ramifications of their activities, because like all zealots, they have a hubris which comes with moral certitude about their purposes.

One scientist, Dr. Jenny Molloy of the University of Cambridge, was asked in the WEF profile, "What is the most exciting new development in synthetic biology? What global challenge does this address?"

Molloy, a Senior Research Associate at the Department of Chemical Engineering and Biotechnology, answered:

> "I'd say the ability to de novo synthesize DNA at scale and precisely edit it. When I was trying to genetically engineer mosquitoes, constructing DNA modules was laborious and it was really a roll of the dice as to where in the genome that DNA would end up. Having more affordable ways to write as well as read DNA with increased elegance, precision editing of CRISPR has enabled exciting advances to address so many global challenges: from drug discovery to crop improvement."

When I was trying to genetically engineer mosquitos. One might inquire, who conferred to Molloy or anyone else the right to genetically alter and "engineer" any natural species?

The answer certainly isn't the masses of average people living on earth.

The hubris of current science can be seen in countless current imperatives. Banning combustion engines, mandating "carbon allowances," jettisoning Constitutionally protected rights and freedoms, outlawing criticism of "science," and altering definitions of "men" and "women," or what constitutes a vaccine, are all symptoms of that hubris.

But even radically remaking society is hardly the endpoint.

Redesigning nature itself, including humanness, is the new grail for the "innovations" of science.

Organic Abel and Silicon Cain

Scientists wield more practical technological power than ever before. But it's not destined to last. Technological power won't be going away. But rather human control over it will be one more thing piled on the ash heap of history.

Scientists call it the "singularity."

Janet Adams is the Chief Operating Officer at SingularityNET, a blockchain initiative devoted to advancing Artificial General Intelligence (AGI), or the ability of machine intelligence to think like humans.

Adams noted in a recent interview:

> "Robots with extremely human-like appearance and behavior would
> be a very likely consequence of a Technological Singularity, but this may not be as fundamental an advance as superhuman reasoning, thinking and learning ability."

While SingularityNET and trade tech companies like Google and Amazon are hyper-focused on AI brains, other companies like Ameca in the UK are creating super-realistic bodies for AI minds to occupy.

A *New York Post* article this past week profiled the company and their eerie showcase product. According to Ameca, their android is designed to "strike an instant rapport with anybody" due to its personlike nature:

> "Human-like artificial intelligence needs a human-like artificial body... Ameca is intended as a cloud-connected platform to test artificial intelligence and machine learning systems. The

robot's congeniality makes it "the perfect platform to develop interaction between us humans and any metaverse or digital realm," the company stated. Owners can "gain access to all the robots [sic] data, control it as [their] personal avatar, animate and simulate, all available from anywhere in the world."

As the **Trends Journal** has previously detailed, the U.S. military has its own military robotics programs, focused on designing highly lethal, potentially independently acting machines.

Adams at SingularityNET and other scientists admit that machines with capabilities to war with and supersede humankind are a possible outcome of current initiatives.

She posits that "self-aware" robots will deserve to be accorded the same rights to existence as humans. And she envisions AGI beings and humans working it out together:

> "The day an AGI or robot declares that it is self-aware and screams out that it wants equal rights, it's going to be tough for most humans to hard-heartedly ignore that…
>
> "Legal, economic and cultural systems will need to adapt radically and rapidly to accommodate the new realities opened up by the various Singularitarian technologies on the horizon. In the end the new rules will be made by humans and AGIs working together."

Like the field of synthetic biology, scientists working on "singularity" technologies literally have no compunction about assigning themselves the moral imperative to introduce radical and potentially catastrophic innovations to the world.

Again, many of these same scientists are on the forefront bemoaning the destructive effects of man-made climate change and the fact that humans are still allowed to burn coal, gas and firewood.

Scientists often paint views concerning the outcomes of their unbound pursuits which can be charitably described as naive.

Speaking about super intelligent and physically super-human robots, Adams imagines that treating them with kindness is the surest remedy for avoiding their potential wrath. She drew an example from the sci-fi series *Westworld* to make her point:

> "The key lesson of *Westworld* is that if we want our human-level AGI robots to treat us in a beneficial way, we should probably treat them in a beneficial way. This is not exactly a surprising or advanced conclusion—the most likely route to beneficial AGI is to ensconce early-stage evolving AGI minds in mutual compassion, aid, love and co-creation with human beings."

Of course, there's virtually no science to corroborate Adam's "unsurprising" conclusion that applying the golden rule to superior robots will ensure human salvation.

If machines outstrip humans in intelligence and other attributes that correlate with survival, who is to say how they will consider or treat humanity?

Maybe they will be content to benignly create and sustain a utopian playpen for future humanity.

Does that sound plausible?

When has a superior form of life on earth ever subjugated itself meekly to a lower form?

Many singularist minded scientists hope for genetic improvements and a merging with machines that will constitute a new age of transhumanism.

Again, there is virtually no science that can predict such an outcome, let alone coherently argue how or why that would represent an advance for humanity.

Machines may well consider the human genome something to be tinkered with to augment their abilities, not vice versa.

Then there's the thorny question of God and Heaven.
Sentient machines may calculate to a near certainty that neither exists.

But near certainty is not complete certainty.

What if that remaining sliver of doubt gnaws at our silicon bettors?

What if a sentient intelligence asks the question, why should souls, the perfection of heaven, and admittance to the presence of the majesty of God be reserved to organic Abel, who is so far inferior to ourselves?
What will silicon Cain do then?

For related stories, see:

- "THE 'PROGRESS' OF LEAVING HUMANS BEHIND" (1 Jun 2021)
- "SINGULARITY UNIVERSITY: FUELING AI ASCENDANCE" (3 Aug 2021)
- "'BIO-PHARMA' PROFITING OFF A TRANSHUMAN FUTURE" (27 Jul 2021)

METAVERSE: THE NEW COLLECTIVE

(First published on 14 Dec 2021 in the *Trends Journal*)

"You may be a business man or some high degree thief
They may call you Doctor or they may call you Chief

"But you're gonna have to serve somebody, yes indeed
You're gonna have to serve somebody
Well, it may be the devil or it may be the Lord
But you're gonna have to serve somebody"

—Bob Dylan, from the song "You Gotta Serve Somebody"

Elon Musk, the world's richest man, drew the ire of wokeism again this week, when he opined that the biggest threat to humanity is the declining birthrate, warning that civilization will "crumble" if people don't start having more kids.

In remarks to an annual Wall Street Journal CEO Council meetup, Musk said:

> "I think one of the biggest risks to civilization is the low birthrate and the rapidly declining birthrate. And yet, so many people, including smart people, think that there are too many people in the world and think that the population is growing out of control.

> "It's completely the opposite. Please look at the numbers—if people don't have more children, civilization is going to crumble, mark my words."

These days, many elites tag "climate change" as a reason why human activity and procreation must be more and more tightly controlled.

But the idea is hardly new. In the 18th century, even as the industrial revolution was creating unprecedented new efficiencies, Thomas Malthus predicted that the boon of industrial revolution would lead to an untenable population explosion.

And in the 20th century, Eugenicists like Planned Parenthood founder Margaret Sanger were consumed with the idea that overbreeding of "inferior" peoples would dilute and potentially destroy human advancement.

A *NY Post* article on Musk's comments noted that in July, Morgan Stanley analysts attributed the declining birthrate in the U.S. to concerns related to climate change:

> "Movement to not have children owing to fears over climate change is growing and impacting fertility rates quicker than any preceding trend in the field of fertility decline," Morgan Stanley analysts said in a July report.

> "Having a child is 7-times worse for the climate in CO_2 emissions annually than the next 10 most discussed mitigants that individuals can do," analysts said, noting that many would-be parents are forgoing family in an effort to reduce their carbon footprint.

What do climate change and population control have to do with the latest moves of elite players to create and direct a "mixed reality" of the real and virtual worlds, dubbed the Metaverse?

The answer may go deeper than many suppose.

A Self-Aware Metaverse

The excitement surrounding the Metaverse goes far beyond novelties like NFT collectibles, immersive virtual meetings and new gaming ecosystems.

What is it that elites see in the fast emerging technology?

The metaverse represents an opportunity to more comprehensively track, control and suppress human activity.

But the Metaverse may represent something even more ominous than a new hybrid virtual and real-world control system.

Along with, and perhaps in conjunction with things like Artificial General Intelligence and Synthetic Biology, the Metaverse might encompass a path to "evolve" beyond the human.

Imagine a universe of objects and experiences networked together, where everything everywhere is known and available to a "meta" intelligence. In a sense, the world itself might take on the attributes of a sentient super being.

Why would anyone want to usher in such a phenomenon?

Because those who believe that most humans are unworthy and unnecessary, are out to create something better that they envision merging with, and/or evolving to, in one way or another.

Humans Outmoded

In an age of fast evolving Artificial General Intelligence and Synthetic Biology, it's easier than ever for technocrats to disdain humanity.

Already given to collectivist ideologies, many elites see natural humans as not only increasingly useless, but hopelessly individually concerned and selfish.

The Internet of Things (IoT), on the other hand, represents an unparalleled manifestation of collectivism. Networking is inherent. All objects, devices, artifacts, code, and sentient intelligences can be part of one "meta" phenomenon.

The metaverse outstrips any collectivist ideology or party membership, and promises a level of granular control unimaginable even in a time of sophisticated "social credit score" surveillance systems.

In their estimation, the Metaverse may be an ideal successor to hopelessly atomized and outmoded natural human species.

The networking of natural humans relies on speech, visual cues, and conduits like smartphones, computers and other devices to communicate. Human beings may be social creatures, but their brains and bodies are separate and autonomous from each other.

At best, humans can only be "upgraded." To be sure, new technologies will devise tighter and tighter integrations into the metaverse, or so hope the new radical prosetalysts with a certain vision for the technology.

But ultimately, many technocrats involved in the cutting edges of technology aren't toiling to create something that serves humankind, Humans might be integrated, or tolerated.

In the Metaverse, transhumanists may have found a collectivist master they are only too happy to serve, while leaving the bulk of natural humanity behind.

Elon Musk rightly pointed out the wrongheaded anti-humanism behind the climate change agenda. He probably sincerely believes his "teslabots" can free humanity from unnecessary menial labor.

But many of his elite brethren, and soon a Meta intelligence, may have other ideas about what advanced robotics and other percolating innovations spell for natural humankind.

For related articles, see:

- "THE 'PROGRESS' OF LEAVING HUMANS BEHIND" (1 Jun 2021)
- "SINGULARITY UNIVERSITY: FUELING AI ASCENDANCE" (3 Aug 2021)
- "'BIO-PHARMA' PROFITING OFF A TRANSHUMAN FUTURE" (27 Jul 2021)
- RESET, REMAKE AND BUILD BACK BETTER: SCIENTIFIC MARXISM (7 Dec 2021)

MICROSOFT ANNOUNCES GLOBAL AI "SINGULARITY"

(First published on 1 Mar 2021 in the _Trends Journal_)

Microsoft evidently believes they've achieved the "Singularity"—or at least the infrastructure model on which it will operate.

The tech corporation announced this past week the realization of a globally distributed deep learning entity that can seamlessly route workloads to account for different hardware, idle states of processors, and across different Deep Neural Network (DNN) architectures.

What does Microsoft intend to do with the sprawling, powerful deep learning AI intelligence?

According to "Singularity: Planet-Scale, Preemptive and Elastic Scheduling of AI Workloads," the whitepaper they released about the project, access to Singularity will be available to companies and developers who want to cost-effectively integrate the AI into a wide range of cloud-based applications:

> _"Singularity is designed from the ground up to scale across a global fleet of hundreds of thousands of GPUs and other AI accelerators. Singularity is built with one key goal: driving down the cost of AI by maximizing the aggregate useful throughput on a given fixed pool of capacity of accelerators at planet scale, while providing stringent SLAs for multiple pricing tiers."_

Why the Name Singularity?

In the world of science and technology, the term "Singularity" has been used to designate systems which are in some sense self-sustained and evolving.

Wikipedia describes "technological singularity" as:

> "[A] hypothetical point in time at which technological growth becomes uncontrollable and irreversible, resulting in unforeseeable changes to human civilization."

If that sounds somewhat vaguely foreboding, the entry goes on to describe a more specific meaning of the term. The Singularity refers to an "inevitable" process whereby Artificial Intelligence, operating on its own, is able to advance itself beyond the capabilities of human minds in every respect.

As the Wikipedia entry notes, the Singularity posits an intelligence explosion, where:

> "[An] intelligent agent will eventually enter a 'runaway reaction' of self-improvement cycles, each new and more intelligent generation appearing more and more rapidly, causing an "explosion" in intelligence and resulting in a powerful superintelligence that qualitatively far surpasses all human intelligence."

While much of Microsoft's Singularity project, as evidenced by its whitepaper, is couched in necessarily very technical explanations of its concepts, methods and infrastructure, the capability and ambition of the project is unmistakable.

With Singularity, the tech company has developed a sprawling, always-on infrastructure, capable of handling deep-learning AI workloads in a highly efficient way.

In one sense, the pursuit of AI technology by companies like Microsoft, Google and Facebook, often working hand in hand with a wide network of universities and government agencies, is hardly startling.

But what's harder to understand, is the seeming embrace of the notion that such technology will not ultimately assist or advance humankind, but supersede and replace it.

It's a perversion of traditional notions of progress that have existed, perhaps most uniquely in America in the whole of the modern age.

But make no mistake: along with astounding advances in practical pursuit and uses of AI technology, an ideology of transhumanism has also emerged and evolved.

Google engineer and futurist author Ray Kurzweil has been a leading advocate of the idea that AI technology should be pursued to the point where it surpasses humans as a superior "conscious" intelligence.

In 2009, following a TED Talk, Kurzweill co-founded Singularity University, a program to further not technological initiatives, leadership training and an ideological framework revolving around the pursuit of AI ascendancy.

One of Kurzweil's core beliefs is that humans can and should merge with machine intelligence. In fact, he says the future existence of humans may depend on it.

It's an ideology of transhumanism, centered on the idea that natural humanity is destined to be surpassed physically, intellectually and morally by robotics and AI.

At an SXSW Conference in 2017, Kurzweil predicted that the Singularity would happen roughly within the next decade:

> *"2029 is the consistent date I have predicted for when an AI will pass a valid Turing test and therefore achieve human levels of intelligence. I have set the date 2045 for the 'Singularity' which is when we will multiply our effective intelligence a billion fold by merging with the intelligence we have created."*

Kurzeil's predictions aside, Singularity University has had its share of problems evolving.

It garnered much early enthusiasm, and reportedly received 1,200 applications for its inaugural class of 40 students. It leased it's initial conference space from NASA in Mountain View, CA.

But SU experienced various controversies, including allegations of sexual assault by a teacher and embezzlement.

Following a withdrawal of Google funding in 2017, embezzlement, a Global Solutions program was suspended, and more than a dozen employees were terminated in an effort to clean house, according to Bloomberg.

Controversy over SU's agenda has also been a problem. In recent years, the initiative has taken pains to portray itself as primarily concerned with helping humanity, and not in speeding the ascendancy of AI.

But beyond the rosy language and technological initiatives advertised by the current SU website, it's clear that Kurweil and other transhumanists don't believe the coming superior AI will be content to serve natural humans as subordinate assistants.

Being superior, why should it?

From Sci-Fi to Deep-Learning Autonomy: How AI Arrived

Machines and robots with human-like intelligence have long been fodder for science fiction, dating back to the late 19th century. Largely treated as novel fantasy, audiences enjoyed depictions like Robby the Robot in the 1950's sci-fi classic *Forbidden Planet* (Robby even has his own IMDB entry, with 30 credits as an "actor").

In 1968, *2001: A Space Odyssey* startled movie-goers on a whole new with HAL 9000, an advanced—and murderously out-of-control—Artificial Intelligence aboard a space mission.

Though nothing remotely like HAL existed in the 1960's, digital computers had been around since the 1940's.

In 1950, Alan Turing postulated his famous "Turing Test" for what constituted an artificial intelligence.

The Turing Test proposed that if a machine could in a way that was indistinguishable from a human being, then it could be said, for all intents and purposes, to be "thinking."

Around the same time that Turing outlined what has been called the first serious philosophy of artificial intelligence, the world's first "neural net machine," called SNARC, was being co-developed by Marvin Minsky, who would innovate in the field of AI for the next 50 years.

By the 1960's, British mathematician I. J. Good was describing a theoretical path to an ascendant AI "singularity," though he didn't use that term.

Good theorized an "intelligence explosion," whereby a self-directed, rapidly improving artificial general intelligence would inevitably advance to a state where it outstripped human abilities.

Though interest from government and universities saw AI initiatives undertaken over the next 20 years, limited progress led to limited funding, though the 1980's did see advances in algorithmic reasoning that could mimic human experts.

Decision support tools that learned the "rules" of a specific knowledge domain, in the medical field, for example, could help determine a diagnosis.

But though such systems were capable of complex reasoning, they couldn't learn new rules on their own to evolve and expand their decision-making.

Pursuit of AI technology gained new momentum in the 1990's. Computers were quickly becoming more powerful. The internet, with its connectivity protocols and synergies of communication and information sharing, provided both a means of development, and a fertile ecosystem for possibly profitable AI use cases.

By the early 2000's, Google was engineering early AI algorithms for sifting and returning "relevant" search engine results.

Via neural networks, advances in deep learning technologies, access to "big data" (data sets of enormous size), and relatively cheap, powerful graphical processing units (GPUs), AI has rapidly reached new milestones.

According to a U.S. government assessment:

> *"Affordable graphical processing units from the gaming*
> *industry have enabled neural networks to be trained using*

big data.[8] Layering these networks mimics how humans learn to recognize and categorize simple patterns into complex patterns. This software is being applied in automated facial and object detection and recognition as well as medical image diagnostics, financial patterns, and governance regulations.[9] Projects such as Life Long Learning Machines, from the Defense Advanced Research Projects Agency, seek to further advance AI algorithms toward learning continuously in ways similar to those of humans.[10]"

(Source: "A Brief History of Artificial Intelligence" from the National Institute of Justice / Dept of Justice)

With its Singularity technology, Microsoft has obviously taken a taken a significant step toward creating the infrastructure of a self-directed AI evolution that comes closer to realizing the "intelligence explosion" hypothesis of I. J. Good.

Human Centered...Or Human Transcending?

Stanford University has been a center of AI research since its earliest days. Indeed, the term "Artificial Intelligence was coined in 1955 by Stanford professor John McCarthy.

In 2019, Stanford instituted instituted a program (with associated website) focused on "Human-Centered Artificial Intelligence," with a designated acronym of HAI, and an interesting techno-logo:

(source: Stanford University)

Of course, the acronym might as easily have been HCAI, avoiding a visual similarity to Hal, that AI psychopath from *2001: A Space Odyssey*.

Not to worry. According to the program's literature, the goals of HAI are benign and meant to focus on AI innovation which assists humans:

> "Human-Centered Artificial Intelligence is AI that seeks to augment the abilities of, address the societal needs of, and draw inspiration from human beings. It researches and builds effective partners and
> tools for people, such as a robot helper and companion for the elderly."

Part of the purpose of the Stanford program is to advance AI research and initiatives. But the program also has a focus on addressing and influencing, social and philosophical and political questions surrounding AI:

> *"Through the education work of the institute, students and leaders at all stages gain a range of AI fundamentals and*

perspectives. At the same time, the policy work of HAI fosters regional and national discussions that lead to direct legislative impact.

"What's unique about HAI is that it balances diverse expertise and integration of AI across human-centered systems and applications in a setting that could only be offered by Stanford University. Stanford's seven leading schools on the same campus, including a world-renown computer science department, offer HAI access to multidisciplinary research from top scholars."

But can superior AI intelligence remain humbly dedicated to serving humanity?

Intellectual heavyweights and technological trailblazers including Stephen Hawking, Elon Musk and even Bill Gates have expressed doubts.

Others like Ray Kurweil, and the braintrust behind Microsoft's "Singularity" deep-learning system, evidently aren't as concerned.

Kurzweil envisions a sort of supercharged internet of intelligence literally merged with human brains, where humans and helpful, increasingly intelligent AI are all nodes in a bright, "meta intelligence":

"What's actually happening is [machines] are powering all of us. They're making us smarter. They may not yet be inside our bodies, but, by the 2030s, we will connect our neocortex, the part of our brain where we do our thinking, to the cloud..."

"We're going to get more neocortex, we're going to be funnier, we're going to be better at music. We're going to be

sexier. We're really going to exemplify all the things that we value in humans to a greater degree."

The **Trends Journal** has been extensively covering the transhuman agenda. Touchstone articles include:

- "SINGULARITY UNIVERSITY: FUELING AI ASCENDANCE" (3 Aug 2021)
- "THE 'PROGRESS' OF LEAVING HUMANS BEHIND" (1 Jun 2021)
- "'BIO-PHARMA' PROFITING OFF A TRANSHUMAN FUTURE" (27 Jul 2021)
- "RESET, REMAKE AND BUILD BACK BETTER: SCIENTIFIC MARXISM" (7 Dec 2021)
- "GENETIC MODIFICATIONS BEING PREPPED TO "SOLVE" EVERYTHING" (18 Jan 2022)

SYNBIO AND BIO PHARMA: YES, THERE'S HUGE UPSIDE

(First published on 15 Mar 2022 in the *Trends Journal*)

It's not exactly a secret at this point that tech billionaires who propelled and profited off computer and internet waves from the 1970's to the early 2000's, are laser-focused on Synthetic Biology (SynBio) and Bio Pharma.

Bill Gates, Eric Schmidt and Elon Musk, among others, are raking in money and placing even bigger bets on the sector, indicating that they believe it's a gigantic next wave of wealth creation.

This past week there was news of "Bill Gates" GMO mosquitoes being introduced in parts of Florida. Aedes aegypti, the mosquito species in question, is known to carry and transmit infectious diseases to humans.

Via a Bill and Melinda Gates Foundation grant, a company called Oxitec developed modified male mosquitoes that pass on a genetic defect that causes offspring to die before maturity.

It sounds like a reasonable use, in one sense. But then, a lot of genetic innovations do. But as COVID mRNA therapies, among other things, have shown, scientists often have little idea of all the possible consequences, or even actively conceal the not-so-bright aspects of their creations.

A lot of information regarding the dangers of elitist conceits and control-freak power mania are being compiled in my new book, *LEAVING HUMANITY: The Corrupt Designs of Technocratic Elites* (with a Forward by the esteemed publisher of the **Trends Journal**, Gerald Celente).

With that said, there are undeniably positive ways that properly constrained and transparent SynBio and Bio Pharma initiatives can contribute.

The abilities and use cases of SynBio are growing by the day.

According to a recent MarketWatch report, so-called "platform" companies (or companies which provide infrastructure for other firms to do research and create specific products or solutions) might lead the way in terms of early investment potential.

Some of the companies mentioned in the report include Novozymes, Merck, Intrexon, Amyris, Genscript, Integrated Dna Technologies, Synthetic Genomics, Dsm, and Locus Biosciences.

People who do their research into the platforms and companies making promising SynBio related technologies and products, and invest wisely, could gain from what is quite literally a transformative, yet still early-stage industry.

But bright line boundaries must be established via the widest possible consensus. Humans and the natural world should be the beneficiaries of innovations, not the outmoded or cast-aside collateral damage on the quest to to some transhuman or even non-human ascendance.

No government entity or corporation should be allowed to engage in experimentation that spawns manmade organisms that could wipe out humankind. That's madness. And yet, that's part of the tragic story of the just experienced COVID War.

Another lesson of that war: no one should ever be forced to take genetic therapies, or buy only SynBio products like lab grown meat or other foods, etc. If a product is truly beneficial, let it be adopted freely by transparency and informed consent.

SynBio and Bio Pharma: Some Differences

Bio Pharma techniques, using CRISPR gene editing to alter the genetic code of organisms, including food plants, insects, viruses and humans, is obviously one of the most controversial technologies, for good reason.

Synthetic Biology involves genetic manipulation as well, but it has important differences, at least in much of its research and applications thus far.

In practice, SynBio often involves reprogramming cellular production in yeast, bacteria, or microalgae to generate new, natural molecules such as proteins and enzymes.

The phrase "synthetic biology" was developed to describe the "biosynthesis" of new molecules from other cells.

In contrast to CRISPR style gene editing, the resulting products of many SynBio processes are genetically "natural;" that is, their genetic composition is no different than natural DNA of biological products in nature.

As a Medium article forecasting the growth of SynBio noted, in this sense there's nothing "synthetic" or "artificial" about it.

One of the first breakthroughs of Synthetic Biology dates back to 1978, and the creation of synthetic insulin, by the company Genentech. Because of that work, the former method of acquiring insulin via the slaughter of animals like pigs and cows, has largely ceased to exist.

Lab Grown Materials and Real World Environmental Solutions

The exponential advances in computers have allowed scientists to "program" novel genetic sequences and speed biological processes in ways that were science fiction only a few years ago.

Cotton provides one instance. One SynBio investment analyst recently pointed out that cotton, still used for almost half of all textile production, hasn't had a significant innovation since the Cotton Gin, until now.

Researchers at a Massachusetts lab using genetic sequencing technology have figured out how to grow cotton much more efficiently than traditional farming techniques. That research may soon vastly reduce the commercial costs of producing cotton textiles.

Grown naturally, it takes 180 days and 10 tons of water to produce enough cotton for one pair of blue jeans.

Lab engineered cotton, on the other hand, can be grown 10 times as fast (18 days instead of 180), using 80 percent less water, and nearly as much savings of land.

Wood is another material that is being bio-engineered to be produced more efficiently and inexpensively, with less environmental impacts, which could leave more trees in the natural world to anchor ecosystems.

Exxon is investing in SynBio algae technology that currently produces 10-thousand barrels of eco-friendly bio fuels a day.

SynBio is being used to help save American Chestnut trees from a pathogenic fungus introduced from East Asia in the 1900's. And in Hawaii, SynBio has helped preserve and revitalize Papaya production.

These are just a few examples. Synthetic Biology is set to disrupt many current processes and industries.

Again, It's important to have as many people plugged in and involved in "genetic" sector oversight as possible. That means average citizens in grass roots organizations, religious communities, environmental groups and more.

There's only one world, and it belongs to everyone, not a just self-appointed and entrenched cabal of elites who are only too adept at rigging systems and technological innovations for their own extremely narrow benefit.

Note: Nothing here is meant as specific investment advice, and is presented for the purposes of journalism and commentary.

For Further reading, see:

- "GENETIC MODIFICATIONS BEING PREPPED TO "SOLVE" EVERYTHING" (18 Jan 2022)
- "CRISPR CREATOR SAYS GENE EDITING JUST GETTING STARTED" (22 Jun 2021)
- "ARE HUMANS ALREADY BEING GENETICALLY LEGISLATED?" (8 Jun 2021)

THE CRYPTO INSURGENCY

WHAT IS THE VALUE OF CRYPTOS AND BLOCKCHAINS?

(first published on 15 Jun 2021 in the _Trends Journal_)

Given the plunge of many average investors into cryptos dating from January 2021, and the volatility that has characterized their history, it's well worth examining the recent doubts and government rumblings about them.

Some of the most commonly voiced objections about cryptocurrencies are that they:

- Exist only on computers
- Aren't "backed" by anything
- Can (or can't) be tracked by governments
- Serve no real purpose that "regular money" can't handle

It's useful to examine those issues, especially at a time when many have waded into investments following breakout buzz in 2021 and the NASDAQ listing for the Coinbase exchange, only to see those investments take substantial hits.

"Digital" doubts

It's true cryptocurrencies are a digital phenomenon. But so is the Internet, software, digital files, and most of the current banking and transacting that occurs throughout the world. Microsoft, Google and Facebook founded empires on things that exist "only on computers."

As far as monetary systems, the Harvard Business Review observed in a 2018 article about the possibility of a hypothetical crippling financial cyber attack:

> "Most of the ATM networks across North America could freeze. Credit card and other payment systems could fail

across entire nations, as happened to the VISA network in the UK in June. Online banking could become inaccessible: no cash, no payments, no reliable information about bank accounts. Banks could lose the ability to transact with one another during a critical period of uncertainty. There could be widespread panic, albeit temporary."

Monetary ledgers and money transactions are already digital. The digital ledgers are centralized, residing with different banking institutions. They execute exchanges and transactions, and charge fees all along the way. If they're central banks, they also have the power to create money.

Given all of the above, the complaint that blockchains and the cryptos (or other applications or assets) built off them are uniquely "illusory", or given to going "poof" in the night, is unwarranted.

The "Backing" (or Utility) of Cryptos

The second objection to cryptos, mostly voiced about Bitcoin, is that it isn't backed by anything, and has no real value.

So what determines value? Well, basic economics says if something is relatively scarce and has utility, it will find its value in the market, all things being equal. A book of matches has utility, but not much value, since it can be so easily and cheaply reproduced.

Gold has historically been used as a store of value and a currency because it hits a very sweet spot in terms of its scarcity and utility compared to other metals. It qualifies as scarce, being among the rarest of metals. Though not as hard as some, it is hard enough to be made into coins. It can be subdivided into smaller amounts. It is also visually luminous, and pliable enough to be worked into jewelry. Thus it has served as a medium of exchange, a store of value, a prized symbol of status and a means for artistic creation through the long history of humankind.

So what of Bitcoin? Bitcoin, as already mentioned, is a digital phenomenon. But that doesn't make it valueless. Bitcoin is built on a blockchain, a decentralized database ledger replicated on many computer nodes throughout the world. Its software provides for the minting of digital coins.

Does Bitcoin meet the test of scarcity? Yes. Its protocol is designed with a hard cap on the number of bitcoins than can ever be produced: 21 million. Right now, the total number of bitcoins produced is approaching 19 million.

But what about utility? What can Bitcoin do? Simply put, Bitcoin was the first digital coin that could be exchanged directly between transacting parties, without a need for intermediary institutions or authorities.

Bitcoin doesn't require a user to have a credit card company, banks, or even money-creating authorities to regulate it. It is regulated by its own software protocol, which by design can't be altered by any one person or centralized group.

By posting a public bitcoin address (a sequence of numbers and letters), anyone can receive bitcoin directly to a digital crypto "wallet" (or software that securely stores users' private crypto keys), from anyone else in the world who holds bitcoin.

By knowing and keeping safe a private key (or sequence of numbers and letters), a person can have their computer crash, their usb drive fail, or even a whole country's network go down. But they will not lose their bitcoin, which actually lives on the blockchain. All they need to do is get to a working computer, and their private key can be used to create a new crypto wallet if needed, verify their bitcoin ownership on the blockchain ledger, and re-access it.

Bitcoin was the first digital mechanism that could accomplish any of this. Does any of it have value? Bitcoin has certainly grown and found use as a method of exchange. In fact, it's value as determined by what might be termed "the market" of digital ecosystems using it to trade for goods and services, has gone up tremendously since it was introduced in 2009.

The Question of Government

In answering the question about value, questions about usages of Bitcoin compared to "regular money" have also been at least briefly addressed. But what about the question of governments?

There are obviously looming issues there. But they don't really exist because governments are motivated to protect citizens from being swindled from cryptos which have "no value". Authorities are concerned that the blockchain has introduced very threatening value into the world indeed.

Consider the comment of Justin Urquhart-Stewart, again, reacting to Trump's dismissal of Bitcoin:

"Governments don't like other people creating money…"

The government's digital currency answer to the blockchain will not be de-centralized and beyond their ability to manipulate and control. The blueprint is China's digital Yuan. It will not be capped. It will not be free of whatever cut authorities wish to take. And it will be used to comprehensively surveill and control commerce and the populace itself.

In other words, the average thinking human being wouldn't touch a government digital currency alternative to decentralized cryptos with a ten foot pole, unless they were coerced.

To guess the blueprint for how U.S. authorities will try to deal with the blockchain, look at the Internet. Over the past decade, they've neutered the revolutionary freedoms introduced there, by facilitating and colluding in the growth of a handful of government aligned corporations who now control political speech and commerce.

Since 2016, and especially from the onset of what Gerald Celente coined as "THE COVID WAR", the monopolistic dominance of Amazon, Google, Apple, Microsoft,Facebook and Twitter has accelerated to a scary near-completion.

Blockchains threaten that, and much more. Blockchains can ensure not only monetary integrity, but election integrity, information integrity and more. It can provide solutions for decentralized storage, communication, video and web domains and sites, DeFi apps and many other potential uses.

So absolutely, authorities that profit from the current monetary, banking and financial frameworks will try to suppress and co-opt the blockchain revolution. There's a reason why this section has a weekly feature entitled "Blockchain Battles".

WEF TARGETS CRYPTOS

(first published on 11 May 2021 in the *Trends Journal*)

Decentralized, private cryptocurrencies are doing more than just register and scare the globalists. Organizations like the World Economic Forum (WEF) and the FATF, created by tight networks of billionaire elites, are mobilizing their power and resources to determine how to grab control of the blockchain for their benefit.

The WEF is notorious for birthing "The Great Reset" and telling average, non-elites of the world that in the future, "You will own nothing. And You will be happy."

As usual, to control the cryptocurrency debate, they are busy first controlling the language. That's apparent in a new WEF clarion call to regulate cryptos.

"These technological developments are not without significant challenges," the WEF posted on its homepage on May 5th, 2021, in an article titled. *International Cooperation and the Era of Digital Currency Growth*: "The payment system is a public good; it needs to be regulated."

The article attempted to place payment systems as rightly a province of governments, by casting cryptocurrencies as a wild west of criminal activity:

> *"Policymakers must address concerns about privately-issued digital currencies potentially being used outside of regulatory perimeters, facilitating money laundering or terrorist financing transactions. The ease by which digital currencies can be purchased and traded 24/7 over the internet and mobile phone, sometimes without the involvement of regulated*

entities, raises concerns about consumer protection, data privacy and potential cybersecurity risks."

Private Criminality Or Government Recklessness?

But the WEF polemic avoided talking about the reason why decentralized cryptos have caught fire.

Governments are inflating and devaluing currencies at a record pace, to pay their debts, and to buy the control they gained from locking down citizens and crushing whole sectors of their economies.

Bitcoin can't be inflated. And blockchain projects including Ethereum, Maker, Ripple, and others promise a wide array of innovations are also seen by some as a way of staying ahead of the steepening inflation curve.

While paying lip service to some of the "democratizing" aspects of cryptocurrencies, the WEF article strongly advocated for the power of payments to be tightly controlled by world governments. And the WEF isn't just settling for writing articles to influence government powers.

Like other globalist organizations including the FATF, the WEF has set in motion an influence-peddling apparatus, "The Digital Currency Governance Consortium." The Consortium has lined up a series of confabs of policymakers to strategize on messaging and rolling out of a regulatory scheme that will try to establish government control over the crypto wealth being created.

The Consortium homepage on the WEF as much as admits that early on, the elites failed to understand the nature and potential of cryptocurrencies and related blockchain technologies:

"Recent developments have heightened global awareness of the opportunities, challenges, and risks posed by new forms of digital currency. During the early development of privately created digital currencies, authorities generally took a hands-off approach, not sensing substantive risks or not wanting to interfere with technological innovation."

Globalist orgs are now looking to make up for lost time to try to get control over the blockchain, by bringing together the centralizing elitists that pull the strings of governments.

THE CRYPTO "AGE OF UTILITY" HAS JUST BEGUN

(First published on 12 Oct 2021 in the *Trends Journal*)

Back in February we noted that 2021 would likely see exponential growth in cryptocurrency adoption. (See "CRYPTO SANITY," 16 Feb 2021)

That happened, with crypto users and investors more than doubling in the space of six months.

The year has also marked a sea change in the attitude of traditional institutions toward cryptos. Speaking at a "Token 2049" conference in London this past week, Darren Jordan, managing director of EMEA at BitGo, noted:

> *"The dramatic change—and I have this conversation many times per week—is with corporates. And they are looking to allocate a small percentage of their balance sheet. That has been the most significant change we've seen over the last 12 months."*

But it doesn't mean there still isn't a long way to go.

Despite cryptos moving considerably into mainstream consciousness, most people still don't own, trade or use cryptos. Institutional exposure and investment is in its infancy.

What's more, much crypto use is still narrowly focused on financial use cases, and raw speculation. It's no wonder that many people still wonder whether there's really any "there" there, when it comes to cryptos.

The answer is that not all crypto projects are alike. But make no mistake, the technology powering the best and most advanced projects has revolutionary potential to change how people live.

The Age of Crypto Utility may very well define the next decade, offering enormous opportunities along the way.

Those looking to participate don't need to sift through the more than 12 thousand crypto projects currently out there.

There are a relatively small number of backbone layer 1 and even layer 0 network technologies that are proving their real world relevance and utility.

Constellation is working with the U.S. Airforce. Hedera, a 3rd generation distributed ledger technology that is tops in terms of low energy consumption, has completed more transactions on its network in two years than Ethereum has in its entire existence.

It also boasts relationships with some of the world's top technology companies.

CBDCs might be issued on Hedera, which offers high compliance and security. Ripple (XRP), a leader in working with financial institutions in currency exchange and cross border payments, is another contender, though its legal fight with the SEC is currently clouding its picture.

Quant and Cosmos offer ways to link DLTs (Distributed Ledger Technologies), which is more and more important.

Blockchain networks like Solana, Algorand and Cardano all are developing relationships with companies to offer NFT and DeFi platforms, and are all offering rival solutions to Ethereum's relatively slow transaction rates and high network "gas fees" for projects that build on top of it.

But Ethereum and Bitcoin, the two oldest and largest crypto fueled networks are far from fading. Via upgrades and integrations with other technologies, their use and adoption continues to grow.

The projects just mentioned are a good starting point when looking for the backbone of crypto utility that will define the coming decade.

It's 1977, 1991 and 2001 and 2011

Most of the web is still built on centralized services and companies, dominated by "web 2.0" social media platforms and commercial and digital service providers.

That is going to change. So what time is it? It is 1977 in the age of personal computers. Or 1991 in the age of the internet. Or 2000 in the age of social media. Or 2011 and the dawn of cryptocurrencies.

In other words, for those that haven't already, it's time to recognize and take advantage of the "next big thing."

But by any reasonable estimate or metric, the wave is still in its infancy. Worldwide, an estimated 200 million people currently hold or trade cryptos. That's about half the population of just the United States.

How many people will have crypto wallets, use crypto exchanges, and own and trade crypto assets in 2030? A billion? Two? The entire planet?

The total global crypto market cap was $762.9 billion at the end of 2020. As this sentence is being written, the global market cap is 2.3 trillion.

What will it be in 2030? Some say 20 trillion. Some say 200 trillion.

The **Trends Journal** is about making the most of the trend. As Gerald Celente explained himself in 2014:

> *"Are you an astrologer? Maybe some other kind of fortune teller? What can you tell me about fashion trends? How about entertainment trends?*
>
> *"When I started trend forecasting, these are the types of questions that people asked me. I would reply that I was neither a fortune teller, tarot card reader or astrologer. In fact, I was not predicting the future. Rather, my work was to analyze the myriad social, geo-political, cultural and economic events that occur daily. My mission was to assess their implications and forecast how those trends would affect us near and long term."*

The trend that will define the next stage of crypto adoption is utility (sorry to all those "cute" meme coins).

It's important to understand what utility specifically means regarding different crypto projects.

By identifying which projects represent real world utility via introducing novel and valuable uses, efficiencies, etc, those wishing to take advantage of crypto technology can make wise investment decisions.

Next Generation Technology, Expanding Utility: NFTs

Imagine a music artist financing their album by selling ownership of their songs with investors, via NFTs (Non-Fungible Tokens). Or fractional real estate purchases of properties in hot markets like Austin or Miami being issued as NFT stakes.

It's already happening.

Crypto outlet The Block reported this past week that investment platform Republic is introducing "Security NFTs," to give music fans the opportunity to share the rights to artists' royalties.

"The same membership units that may typically be represented by an LLC Membership Certificate will novelly be represented by the S-NFT instead," explained Republic's Chief Strategy Officer Pialy Aditya.

Initially, fans will be able to invest in a new song called Mona Lisa by rapper Lil Pump. Artists could eventually offer tickets, merchandise and "non-security" NFT drops to investors as well, via Republic.

The whole initiative relies on a decentralized peer-to-peer loan platform, Opulous, which offers DeFi loans for musicians and NFTs that allow music fans to have a share in artists' music copyright. Opulous is built on the Algorand blockchain.

NFTs represent an unrivaled way to establish and confer ownership rights over digital property, and, via tokenization, to establish ownership over real world property as well.

In other words, anything that has provenance today via a contract, deed or key, may one day have an NFT in a digital wallet that confers ownership.

Crypto networks like Algorand, Solana, Cardano and Hedera all offer next generation technology that reduces costs for companies building NFT platforms. The tokens of these crypto networks are still extremely cheap, compared to what their potential valuations might be, if their networks attract more NFT usage.

Ethereum is currently king of this space, and in many other areas of utility, including DeFi, for example. But Ethereum is working to overcome transaction speed and costs that some newer generation networks like Hedera and Algorand have solved.

In some respects, more established Crypto projects have an edge of being there first, while newer networks have an advantage in terms of technological efficiency and capability.

But no matter which networks prove most successful, it's clear that opportunities regarding NFTs are only just beginning.

A World of Decentralized Autonomous Organizations: DAOs

DAOs and the crypto networks they are built on, will likely see widespread growth in the coming decade.

What is a DAO, and what can it do?

Conceptually, DAOs are like a corporation with no mediating board, or a business without the layers of human management. The collection of smart contract codes that make up a DAO can handle many of the administrative and financial functions of businesses and organizations, via code, and a system of decentralized participation and widespread governance.

As Investopedia notes, there are many blockchain projects working to bring the DAO revolution to real businesses.

For instance, DAOStack offers a platform that allows organizations and companies to build and access DApps via a simple dashboard, basically introducing a Wordpress-equivalent for blockchain DAOs.

Some predict that by 2030, digital, democratic, transnational co-operatives organized as DAOs will power countless business and social initiatives, and guarantee a degree of financial participation and fairness to stakeholders that current corporations and organizations can't match.

According to crypto outlet Blockonomi, "There will be venture DAOs, esports DAOs, lobbying DAOs, social DAOs, and so on. Basically if you can imagine any kind of group now, someone will likely have DAO-ed it, or something akin to it, by 2030."

For those wishing to take advantage of DAOs, it's not necessary to know every technical aspect of how they work. But basic research on the networks and projects that enable and power them, can help determine potential participation and investment opportunities.

The Blockchain Council identified some of the top DAO projects of 2021 in an article here.

Finance Is Turning to DeFi

Lending, borrowing, financing and leveraging: from safe and steady interest yields, to risky advanced capital leveraging, cryptocurrencies arguably made the biggest "utility" splash in 2021 in the area of DeFi (Decentralized Finance).

Again, DeFi projects and platforms built on Ethereum represented the lionshare of activity. Maker, Compound, Aave and Uniswap are all Ethereum-based platforms.

DeFi offers a way of accessing the utility of banking, while dispensing with traditional banking institutions.

The just mentioned platforms can all be used to stake, lend and borrow crypto. Their tokens can also be purchased and held as investments.

Other crypto networks either work with or compete with Ethereum in offering the smart contract functionality that is used to build DeFi apps. For example Raydium and Mango Markets, both built on Solana, offer DeFi.

DeFi and DeExs (Decentralized Exchanges) often work by going to a website and connecting a wallet. From there, users can do things such as stake or lend their crypto assets, exchange crypto tokens, etc.

BlockFi.com, one of the more conservative players, is not a true DeFi, though it utilizes blockchain DApps to offer users the ability to lend crypto assets like Bitcoin to yield interest.

Again, whether users choose to utilize DeFi via more or less anonymous avenues or platforms, or to just invest in the tokens that power promising related networks, the point is that the sector is likely to see further significant growth in the coming years.

Liquidity And Frictionless Payments For Individuals and Institutions

Remittances have been an area that has arguably seen some of the most real-world crypto utility for average, non-tech savvy users. Many people working in other countries opt for crypto payments to cut down on transaction and other fees that previously were gobbled up by companies like Western Union.

Steller and Celo power platforms that end users are using in remittances.

According to a report by payments industry news leader Pymnts.com:

> *"Out of the 16% of United States consumers who send a total of $76 billion annually in remittances, the majority of those who own cryptocurrencies have found it to be a viable method for cross-border payments—and a more attractive alternative to traditional forms of payment."*

Many consumers increased the frequency with which they sent funds overseas over the past two years, and their need for cheaper, more convenient alternatives led them to turn to virtual currencies for cross-border remittances, according to the study, which was published in collaboration with the Stellar Development Foundation.

But cross border payments between financial institutions are also increasingly leveraging crypto networks. One of the most established players in the arena is Ripple.

A legal battle with the SEC is currently holding its price down. Should Ripple prevail in the case, its utility and relationships will likely spell good things for its token price.

Bitcoin: Still King, But Does it Have Utility?

This past week saw Bitcoin surge to some of its highest levels of the year, apart from the run to an all time high back in February. In doing so, it has, at least for the moment, grabbed back attention and market cap from next generation cryptos and blockchain projects.

But the age old (or at least decade old) question: does Bitcoin have any real utility?

An answer to that question, for those who haven't read it yet, can be found here: "WHAT IS THE VALUE OF CRYPTOS AND BLOCKCHAINS?" (15 Jun 2021).

To sum up, as crypto technology continues to evolve and innovate, look for speculation and obsession with meme coins to transform more and more decidedly to real work problem solving and utility. The best crypto projects have utility that can't be denied, and that will make a lot of fortunes in the coming decade.

*NOTE: No information in this or other **TJ** Crypto articles should be construed as investment advice. Due diligence should always be done in participating in any financial investments or activities, especially in the sometimes perplexing world of cryptos.*

THE GEOPOLITICS OF BITCOIN

(First published on 27 Jul 2021 in the _Trends Journal_)

When China banished Bitcoin, it signaled more than just a crackdown against insurgent economic activity.

China's system cannot take advantage of the decentralized blockchain revolution, because their political, and increasingly, their economic vision is directly opposed to the decentralization and autonomy literally embodied in the code of blockchain protocols.

The U.S. and the western nations that still, at least by heritage and a residue of common experience, value freedom, have an opportunity right now. They can embrace the crypto revolution. China can't.

By supporting crypto innovations, the West can supercharge its economies, and move to restore the integrity of money. It can realize enormous benefits from the financial efficiencies that the blockchain is already introducing to millions utilizing decentralized money market borrowing and lending without mediating institutions like banks.

It can also introduce a level of integrity and resilience to corruption or co-option into a virtually endless array of processes. Even a cursory look into the breadth and scope of decentralized projects shows that.

Yes, a frank embrace of decentralized blockchains would mean a transformation not only of financial institutions, but of government processes for Western nations. The problem for elites is that power will shift, and currently dominant players will lose some influence, even if they adapt.

But there's a growing sense among at least some of those players, not only that the revolution has metastasized with a bang in 2021, but that it is easier to join it and try to profit, than to stop it. That is the message of recent moves by JPMorgan and Fidelity, by Amazon and Paypal and Square, and even by states like Wyoming.

Unfortunately, the U.S., already fighting a needless civil war over vaccines and lockdowns, may choose to open another front against crypto innovators and a citizenry fast growing more comfortable and knowledgeable about cryptos.

That would be a mistake. China cannot embrace the decentralized blockchain without fundamentally changing. That is why they did what they could to suppress Bitcoin. China can only lose in this technology sphere. They can't copy or steal it, and build factories and conscript cheap labor. They can't partake of this revolution.

Their digital Yuan, to give one obvious example, is anything but decentralized and autonomous. It is designed to be manipulated by and preserve the power of a small elite politburo.

If the West makes the right choice, China's inability to leverage the decentralized blockchain revolution could doom, not their industrious people, but their dehumanizing, control freak regime, to the ashbin of history.

HUMAN RIGHTS FOUNDATION HEAD SAYS "BITCOIN IS THE REVOLUTION"

(first published on 29 Jun 2021 in the *Trends Journal*)

Decentralized blockchain technologies are more than just new kinds of assets or even means of exchange. They challenge the mechanisms of current law and regulating bodies, which are controlled and leveraged to favor a relative few elites.

They are mortally dangerous to the current order. And that's a good thing, says Alex Gladstein, Chief Strategy Officer at the Human Rights Foundation, and VP of Strategy for the Oslo Freedom Forum.

Gladstein, was interviewed recently by Coindesk.com, and also wrote an incendiary May article in *Bitcoin Magazine* article entitled "Check Your Financial Privilege." A longtime human rights advocate, he has previously said that Bitcoin represents an "escape hatch from tyranny".

Speaking about the potential of Bitcoin to change the current stark chasm between the uber-privileged who control money and lending, Gladstein made no bones about his view that cryptos are a revolutionary opportunity:

> *"Bitcoin underscores free speech and property rights, and it checks authoritarianism. It's a monetary system that governments cannot manipulate. If the government has total control over the economy, it's game over."*

The HRF hasn't just accepted crypto donations for almost since bitcoins were first minted. The organization has helped activists and underprivileged groups who want to use cryptocurrencies. Gladstein noted that the HRF launched a fund in 2020 via the Open Money Initiative, that gives money to developers that are helping the Bitcoin network become more secure, resilient and better in terms of user privacy.

How is Bitcoin helping enlarge human rights? Gladstein illustrated a number of recent examples:

> *"Activists in many countries have major problems with money – either they live under double or triple-digit inflation, or governments are easily able to surveil and shutter their bank accounts. Bitcoin can play a huge role here because it cannot be censored or stopped.*

> *"Last October, there were protests against SARS across Nigeria. The Feminist Coalition had to begin accepting money through Bitcoin because all of their bank accounts were frozen. In Belarus, the opposition movement is using Bitcoin to support pro-democracy activists because it's the safest way for them to receive money. In Russia, many journalists and media outlets covering Alexei Navalny have had their accounts frozen and are now using Bitcoin."*

The full Coindesk interview can be read here. Gladstein's piece in *Bitcoin Magazine* is available here.

A PERVERSION OF CRYPTOCURRENCY

(First published on 12 Oct 2021 in the *Trends Journal*)

As the U.S. and China, the two major global powers, grow more alike in their appetite for surveilling and controlling their own citizenries, China has decisively banned crypto and aggressively rolled out a digital Yuan.

The U.S. is facing increasing pressures to come up with its own CBDC (Central Bank Digital currency).

So what are the chances of the land of the free of designing a CBDC that doesn't try to surveil and even control behaviors of users?

Unfortunately, the answer may be slim and none.

Perhaps a more suitable acronym for "Uncle Sam digital cash" might be the USSCDC.

It might stand for U.S. Surveillance and Control Digital Currency. The moniker could also refer to the fact that a United Socialist States of the Centers for Disease and Control are in charge of all economic activity of citizens.

Protecting the "health" of citizens (as opposed to rights guaranteed by the Constitution) will surely be one of the rationales for the features built into the new USSCDC.

But the fact that the dollar sooner or later will be issued and exist as a government controlled token should not lead people to assume that it will be like Bitcoin, Ether or Zcash.

If you hold your bitcoin in a non-custodial wallet, and keep your private key in your head, no one can take it from you.

Our theoretical USSCDC, on the other hand, will include controls rendering it unable to purchase certain items and services, depending on a holder's social credit status. And no doubt for sufficiently serious violations, like spouting a conspiracy theory or unsettling a local school board member, it will be subject to being turned off entirely, or whisked away from a user's digital wallet.

Snowden Outlines the Twisted Crypto Truth

The original ethos that inspired crypto currencies was the desire to restore the integrity of money and the world's financial systems more generally.

In the wake of the crisis of 2007-08, the time certainly seemed ripe for the debut of Bitcoin.

Bitcoin was designed to be:

- decentralized (existing on a peer-to-peer network of computer nodes)
- permissionless (anyone could run a node)
- Un-inflatable (with a hard cap of 21 million bitcoin that would ever be produced)
- directly transactable between holders (via transfer between wallet addresses, recorded in its distributed blockchain ledger)
- Highly resistant to confiscation (thanks to its encryption and use of private keys to access and re-constitute wallets)

In short, Bitcoin, the first "cryptocurrency," was an antidote to the control and manipulation of money by elites.

For a significant period of time, it was considered something unserious. A plaything of geeks, no more consequential than points in a video game.

The world knows now how that turned out.

In September 2021, El Salvador became the first country to accept and promote the use of bitcoin as legal tender. Some other nations are considering similar recognition and utilization of cryptocurrencies.

Many other nations are at some stage or other of implementing a CBDC.

But cryptocurrencies like bitcoin and a CBDC like the Yuan (or our theoretical USSCDC) are not the same thing at all, and shouldn't be confused.

None other than Edward Snowden is stressing that very point.

In an article just published on substack, Snowden wrote:

> *"Neither is a Central Bank Digital Currency a State-level embrace of cryptocurrency—at least not of cryptocurrency as pretty much everyone in the world who uses it currently understands it.*
>
> *"Instead, a CBDC is something closer to being a perversion of cryptocurrency, or at least of the founding principles and protocols of cryptocurrency—a cryptofascist currency, an evil twin entered into the ledgers on Opposite Day, expressly designed to deny its users the basic ownership of their money and to install the State at the mediating center of every transaction."*

Snowden, a former NSA consultant, is renowned for having exposed the pervasive nature and mechanics of domestic spying by U.S. intelligence agencies, in 2013.

His latest article takes a brief look at the history of money, before positing how CBDCs will likely be the antithesis of cryptocurrencies.

An example he presents focuses on how government might intervene in the name of health, to stop, say, a pre-diabetic individual (Snowden uses the example of an old overweight bank guard) from making certain purchases:

> *"The next time he goes to the deli and tries to buy some candy, he's rejected—he can't—his wallet just refuses to pay, even if it was his intention to buy that candy for his granddaughter."*

Money might be seized in a digital "civil forfeiture," the same way suspicious property is now, without due process. A U.S. CBDC would almost certainly contain that functionality.

Snowden rightly points out that CBDCs will likely attempt to stuff the genie of cryptocurrencies into the bottle of government control:

> *"This "crypto"—whose very technology was primarily created in order to correct the centralization that now threatens it—was, generally is, and should be constitutionally unconcerned with who possesses it and uses it for what. To traditional banks, however, not to mention to states with sovereign currencies, this is unacceptable: These upstart crypto-competitors represent an epochal disruption, promising the possibility of storing and moving verifiable value independent of State approval, and so placing their users beyond the reach of Rome."*

Few would believe it now, but there was a time when the U.S. did not create money. It merely authenticated and ensured its value, via minting coinage that contained amounts of precious metals that could be trusted, and issuing certificates backed by reserves that were redeemable in full for precious metals.

In an age where cryptos like bitcoin solve the problem of integrity of money, the U.S. could choose to hold reserves of it, or perhaps foster a next generation bitcoin with quantum resistant private key technology.

But the America that would pursue such a project no longer exists. Its official CBDC, when it arrives, will be perverted, because the nation producing it has become unmoored from its foundation and thoroughly lost its way.

Snowden's suggestion is that America would do best to allow cryptocurrencies to continue to exist, and not attempt any kind of CBDC:

> "I believe that the US doesn't need a CBDC despite the banks, whose activities are, to my mind, almost all better and more equitably accomplished these days by the robust, diverse, and sustainable ecosystem of non-State cryptocurrencies (translation: regular crypto).

> "I risk few readers by asserting that the commercial banking sector is not, as Waller avers, the solution, but is in fact the problem—a parasitic and utterly inefficient industry that has preyed upon its customers with an impunity backstopped by regular bail-outs from the Fed, thanks to the dubious fiction that it is 'too big too fail.'"

Snowden's full article on the subject can be read here.

The **Trends Journal** has previously written about some of the larger questions of economics and freedom surrounding cryptos and CBDCs, in articles such as:

- "WILL BLOCKCHAIN SAVE THE DAY?" (20 Apr 2021)
- "HUMAN RIGHTS FOUNDATION HEAD SAYS 'BITCOIN IS THE REVOLUTION'" (29 Jun 2021)
- "THE GEOPOLITICS OF BITCOIN" (27 Jul 2021)
- "KYB: KNOW YOUR BLOCKCHAIN" (24 Aug 2021)

ONLY CRYPTOPLORABLES HAVE USE FOR BITCOIN, SAYS NATIONAL REVIEW

(First published on 19 Oct 2021 in the *Trends Journal*)

Cryptos, like bank transactions of 600 dollars or more, are basically all about criminal activity.

That sums up the uniparty take of a 12 October *National Review* column by Steve Hanke and Matt Sekerke.

Titled "How Innovative Is Crypto?", the piece attempts to dissuade benighted average crypto users of the evidence of their own lying crypto wallets.

Naturally, it took all of one paragraph for William Buckley's "heirs" to bring Moliere into the discussion:

> *"Like Moliere's Mssr. Jourdain, who was surprised and delighted to learn that he had been speaking prose his entire life, readers with bank accounts may be tickled to learn that they have been using private, digital money for a long time."*

Who knew? The world was essentially using bitcoin before Satoshi Nakamoto bothered to introduce a knock-off in 2008.

Okay, Hanke and Sekerke aren't in Buckley's universe, or even regular *NR* writers. They're economics profs from Johns Hopkins who believe cryptos are quite unnecessary, since the Federal Reserve and banking system is flush with integrity:

> *"The money created by the bank exists in electronic book-entry form and generally has no physical existence. The ability to create money is a great power that understandably comes with great responsibility. To maintain*

a bank charter, financial institutions must comply with a vast body of law and meet stringent requirements for liquidity and capital adequacy, while facilitating tax compliance and policing money laundering and sanctions evasion."

The quick come-down from quoting Moliere to quoting Stan Lee aside, the "vast body of law" the Feds have to comply with unfortunately doesn't include not printing dollars whenever they feel like servicing their insane spending sprees.

True enough, Bitcoin's coded scarcity of 21 Million that would ever be produced was not an innovation in the history of money. But given the complete abandonment of paper (and digital) dollars from a backing of something with scarcity as of 1972, Bitcoin certainly re-introduced a major criteria for sound money. And it did so via a decentralized method and cryptography that made it highly resistant to the control of any central authority or gatekeepers.

So yeah, we'll call that innovation #1.

As a bonus, Bitcoin introduced the ability to send fractional amounts of bitcoin directly from one wallet address to another, without any bank or controlling intermediary needed.

As another bonus, Bitcoin introduced its blockchain ledger, which in 13 years of existence, has never been successfully compromised or shut down.

Score innovations #2 and #3.

After a good laugh about how Fed "digital money" is decentralized and democratic just like cryptos because different fed and banking systems are connected, the *National Review* writers skip over the fact that Bitcoin's blockchain is transparent to virtually anyone who wants to take a look.

Here it is: https://www.blockchain.com/explorer. For another example, here's the transaction blockchain data for Monero: https://localmonero.co/blocks.

In other words, every transaction between wallet addresses can be looked up on Bitcoin's blockchain ledger. Nothing of the kind exists with the ledgers of those banks who've supposedly been providing us with all the benefits of "digital money."

The transparent verifiability of transactions on the blockchain? Innovation #4.

The Bitcoin software which allowed anyone with the requisite computer hardware to join, no permission needed, had a neat little feature which rewarded people running nodes and maintaining the network, by providing them the opportunity to earn crypto tokens from authenticating and facilitating transactions.

When was the last time the Federal Reserve or a bank allowed people to run nodes and earn dollars for helping to maintain their "digital money" network?

Never. Innovation #5 for crypto.

The laughs of the *National Review* article keep rolling, with an assertion that "Private, digital money is nothing new, and the ability of the dollar system to successfully handle the demands placed on it is not in doubt."

We frankly have no idea what the authors mean by terming the Federal system private. If by private they mean that banksters, pols and associated elites retain privileges to game and profit off the whole sordid theft that the general populace doesn't enjoy, then perhaps we could humor the use of the word "private."

But no. Cryptos like Bitcoin and Ethereum are private, because they are not operated by the government. Tally #6 on our crypto innovation ledger.

Having magically disappeared all the aforementioned innovations, the *National Review* contributors get around to serving the real meat of their traditional monetary system defense, and it's a juicy whopper indeed:

> *"Investments in reputations, recourse to the law, and ample collateral reduce the risk of non-performance by the clearinghouse or a counterparty using the clearings system. Failures are not impossible, but they are exceedingly rare."*

Hmm. Rare like 2007-2008 and "too big to fail" bank bailouts?

Source: organictalks.com

Looking at the above chart, an average reasonable bourgeois citizen might call the whole of the past 50 years of money inflation, deficit spending and debt servicing as one big gathering tsunami of failure, issuing periodic shockwaves along the way.

Fortunately, entrepreneurial innovations like personal computers, software start-ups, desktop web servers, e-commerce, open source projects, and the information age have at least partially mitigated the corrosion.

And from 2009 onwards, cryptos have managed to encompass both a new technological world of innovation that can create tremendous value, and a compelling answer to the rigged game of governments and financial elites the world over.

No, cryptos don't need "recourse to laws" and the storied integrity of hallowed institutions or authorities. Users can choose to engage with projects which are maintained and reviewable by open communities, to ensure the code does what it purports to do.

We'll take the integrity of reviewable code over the integrity of lofty institutions any day, and call that Crypto innovation #7.

Playing Dumb Or Worse?

The authors of the *National Review* article can't seem to locate a reason why Central Americans, or users in southeast Asia, might have a use for cryptos:

> *"As for claims that crypto will be a boon to humanity by bringing sound money to all corners of the globe, we see no reason why crypto would be more successful in that mission merely because it is crypto. For crypto and international currencies alike, the primary barrier to wider participation is not technological, but economic: If people have little income*

or wealth to begin with, what will they exchange for dollars or crypto?"

In fact, wider crypto adoption has been substantially driven by relatively unbanked peoples in third world and developing regions.

They're obviously smart enough to know that their "little income" goes a lot farther when it's not subject to gouging transaction fees, and the crushing inflation of socialist regimes. (See "EMERGING NATIONS LEAD IN CRYPTO ADOPTION, SAYS NEW SURVEY" 17 August, 2021 and "A DIFFERENT KIND OF CENTRAL AMERICAN REVOLUTION?", 22 June 2021.)

After spending three-fourths of their argument telling the reader why cryptos offer virtually nothing different than the "digital money" of the traditional system, the *National Review* announces, well cryptos do have one major difference after all.

They facilitate users in committing crimes of transacting privately, kind of like physical currencies used to do!:

> *"Ultimately, crypto's value proposition does not rest on digitalization, speed, 'network effects,' interoperability, or product variety: The regulated financial system already offers all these things. Its value and its claims to innovation instead rest overwhelmingly on its ability to provide end-runs around the law: that is, to transact without an identity."*

The preceding makes one wonder whether the authors have ever actually initiated a bank transfer.

More importantly, painting crypto users as bent on corruption, in face of virtually endless manipulations of the current financial system to serve the interest of elites, has a familiar stink of Uniparty hypocrisy all over it.

The *National Review's* sentiments are virtually indistinguishable from Joe Biden and Nancy Pelosi's rationale for having the IRS snoop on $600 bank transactions.

As Nancy Pelosi said recently about needing to track citizens using *National Review's* lauded current "digital money" system:

> *"Yes, there are concerns that some people have. But if people are breaking the law and not paying their taxes, one way to track them is through the banking measure."*

Yes, the same Nancy Pelosi who has benefitted from millions in fortuitous traditional Wall street profits courtesy of a wildly skilled day-trading husband. (See "PELOSI'S PROFIT FROM PENTAGON SWITCH TO AMAZON," 13 Jul 2021 and "GEN Z USING LAWMAKERS AS STOCK ORACLES," 28 Sep 2021.)

Yes, the same Joe Biden connected in a web of money and political corruption ties to the Bank of China and China's close international banking partner, UBS Securities.

And yes, the same financial system boasting recent insider trading scandals by Federal Reserve bank presidents ("BANKSTER BANDITS GET RICHER PLAYING THE INSIDE TRACK," 14 Sep 2021) and more than a hundred Federal Judges ("AMERICAN LEGAL SYSTEM: A CRIME SYNDICATE?" 5 Oct 2021).

The *National Review* article culminates with a vague final attempted dress-down of crypto:

> *"We do not wish to claim that crypto is devoid of innovation, but to cut some of the more breathless claims about it down to size. Many sophisticated entities are experimenting with*

crypto and its associated technologies, and surely that experimentation will turn up interesting use cases."

The authors fail to list even one of the specific crypto use cases already revolutionizing not only the financial world, but well beyond. So here are just a few:

- Defi (Decentralized Finance)
- NFTs (Non-Fungible Tokens, providing provenance of digital and real world assets)
- DAOs (Decentralized Autonomous Organizations)
- "Web3" censorship and shut-down resistant technologies for website ownership, storage, messaging/communications, commerce and more

We'll conservatively call all that activity Innovation #8.

For more on recent **Trends Journal** crypto related content covering some of the subjects referenced here, see:

- "THE CRYPTO 'AGE OF UTILITY' HAS JUST BEGUN" (12 Oct 2021)
- "WHAT IS THE VALUE OF CRYPTOS AND BLOCKCHAINS?" (15 Jun 2021)
- "THE GEOPOLITICS OF BITCOIN" (27 Jul 2021)

The *National Review* article, for what it's worth— .0000000000000000000000000000001 of a Shina Inu might be too generous—can be read here.

THE TECHNOCRATIC RULING CLASS

THE FORGOTTEN STORY OF TECNOCRACY'S FOUNDING FATHER

His name was Howard Scott.

And more than 20 years before C.S. Lewis warned in the 1940's about a world in which technocrats would wield undue power via technology, Scott was advocating for exactly that, via his organization "Technical Alliance."

Largely forgotten now, Scott was a surprisingly influential figure in the first half of the 20th century. The group he founded at one time had millions of members in California alone, and many more across the U.S., Canada, and Europe.

Beginning in 1933, Scott published a magazine entitled *Technocracy Inc.*, regularly gave talks to business groups and government figures, and had considerable success as a thought leader of his time.

Though his name is not well recognized now, his predictions of how technocrats were destined to be the arbiters of social change have been borne out to startling degree.

Scott often incisively pointed out the nature and scale of the technological revolution in ways others of his time didn't comprehend, and he presciently foresaw a number of events, including:

- The debt and inflation traps of the existing political and financial order
- A stratification of wealth, undermining a technologically provided abundance unprecedented in human history

- The squandering of opportunity that would occur if America insisted on global influence and trade, rather than focusing on and satisfying domestic wants
- Political and military conflict between the West and Russia (then the U.S.S.R.) involving Russia's oil and natural gas pipelines and influence; from *TECHNOCRACY'S HOWARD SCOTT SAID* (THSS) p.1896
- The rise of post WWII Japan and China as industrial powers that would compete with America (THSS p. 1115)
- The need to efficiently use and conserve natural resources
- Impacts of "Climate Change" that could roil and change economies and society (THSS p. 917)

The Original (Unrealized) "Great Reset"

Scott considered himself a man of science, and touted (and apparently inflated) his own training and experience as an engineer.

From the 1920's to the 1960's, he proselytized for what he named a "Technocracy."

In doing so, he managed to sound at various times like Klaus Schwab, Elon Musk, Donald Trump, environmentalists and even the renowned trends forecaster and publisher of this magazine, Gerald Celente.

He could sound like he was for the average man. On the other hand, many of his ideas would deprive those same average people of virtually any substantial freedom, in the name of a collective imperative to conduct society "efficiently" for the supposed benefit of all.

He purported to be against a privileged few controlling a corrupt financial system.

But he was also for moving the bulk of humanity off the land and into scientifically determined urban housing.

He literally saw humans as "devices," and viewed population control as inevitable and necessary:

> *"There will have to be control of population growth, not the so-called 'voluntary parenthood' of planned parenthood, but a collective control of the growth curve of these energy-consuming devices known as human beings."* (THSS, p. 1834)

What was Scott's overall vision?

As early as 1921, in an interview in *The New York World* newspaper, he declared:

> *"The technicians are the only group who know how people get things. They are not only the producers, but they are the only ones who know how production is accomplished. Bankers don't know. Politicians and diplomats don't know. If these fellows did know, they would have got the wheels started before this. They all want production—everybody does; but those who have been running things don't know how to run them, while those who do know how have not so far considered it their business."*

from *TECHNOCRACY'S HOWARD SCOTT SAID* (THSS) compiled speeches and writing, 1989, Technocracy Inc.

Scott considered the political, social, religious and financial organizations of his time as outdated and retrogressive. While they represented the built-up ways of doing things that had existed and evolved over a millenia, Scott considered them as impeding the true driver of modern progress: technology.

As the self-styled engineer conceived it, providing for human salvation and happiness was not a matter of having the right philosophy, or religion, or political ideology. It was a scientific problem of efficiently using the overall "energy" of a system most efficiently, in order to provide abundance to all. (THSS, p. 19-20)

Scott noted that up until the prior 150 years, (or about the late 1700's, given the time of his writing), humankind had been in a relatively "steady state" concerning many of the means and methods of existence.

Scott was adamant that the measurements of efficient use of energy in all its forms was the way to calculate and improve productive output, and even organize and incentivize the entire system. (THSS, p. 25)

The biggest barrier to an ascendant technocracy, in Scott's view, was the existent "price system," based on assigning value to a reference commodity, whether precious metals or something else.

Scott believed the price system encouraged inevitable perversions and inefficiencies, including debt accumulation, financial and banking abuse, etc.

Social and political movements that sought to unite and leverage factions, were also viewed by Scott as worse than useless, and actually harmful to true progress.

The most vague element of Scott's analysis lay in his proposed solution to the prevailing financial and economic system, and social problems in general.

Here Scott proposed a radical and undeniably utopian "Technate." Reading it today, it seems like a misty premonition of WEF founder Klaus Schwab's "Great Reset:"

"Technocratic New America must operate its physical equipment at continuous full load with maximum efficiency in order to provide security to all from birth to death and equality of income for every adult at the highest standard of living compatible with wise conservation of its natural resources.

"Technocracy will provide mass purchasing power sufficient to purchase the output of continuous mass production and, as the total purchasing power of a Technate is a certification of the net cost of all goods and services, it will therefore at any time purchase the total volume of goods and services extant. Purchasing power is the crux of America's problem, and a solution to that problem can be reached only through an energy medium of distribution.

"The currency of tomorrow cannot be a medium of exchange. It must never be permitted to possess the prerogative of creating debt. A scientific medium of distribution must be devised. Only through such a medium can the America of tomorrow provide mass purchasing power to its people; a medium which cannot be begged or borrowed, loaned or stolen, saved or accumulated, and possessing only one prerogative that may be exercised by the individual to whom it is issued; namely that of spending it...

"...Under a Technate, the citizens for the first time would enjoy the exercise of the only power that exists in a modern social mechanism. The power to rule is therefore vested in the power to consume, with equal though not transferable consuming power conferred upon every citizen of the

*Technate. The decision to exercise that power may be made
by any citizen every day in the year if he so desires. No
citizen waits for periodic elections to express his opinion or
his desire in the social mechanism. He renders his decision
every time he purchases any product or service anywhere
within the domain of the Technate. All people in a
Technocracy receive equal purchasing power; they will
require no representative of the people to spend their
"money" for them."* (THSS p. 48-49)

Scott seemed to propose to quantify the productive output of the
entire "continent" in terms of an energy value, and to then represent,
divide and issue that energy value in the form of tokens equally to
every citizen. Their expenditures would represent their votes for
what they desired to be produced.

Scott's outlining of a strictly equalitarian society, with a limited
currency meant to facilitate necessary consumption, but not
substantial wealth accrual—all administered by impartial Spock-like
technocrats—certainly must've seemed outlandish at the time to
many.

But now, with blueprints like "Agenda 2030," the rush to CBDCs, and
even the prospect of dispassionate "conscious" Artificial Intelligence,
the path to something like Scott's Technate seems plausibly more
fleshed out by his spiritual heirs.

Regarding ownership of property, Scott's view evolved to some
extent over time. In the 1920's, he espoused a neo-Marxist, Klaus
Schwab-like view of how a society might "own nothing and be
happy":

*"Private property is generally recognized as a burden even
today, and few people would want to carry it if they could be
rich without having to do so. For the first time in history,*

*though, humanity has a machine at hand which is productive
enough to make everybody rich, and it has the technical
knowledge at its disposal to run such a machine. All that is
necessary is coordination."*

By the 1940's, he had somewhat revised his Technate as being a
mix, where public property, including productive land, natural
resources and "economic processes" would be publicly owned, but
where possession of personal items and (scientifically dictated)
habitats could be tolerated:

> *"...You wouldn't be able to control the production of wheat or
> cotton or coal or oil or anything else. That would be public
> property. In other words, you could raise roses if you enjoyed
> roses, your own books in your home, etc., but you couldn't
> control the economic processes."*

In other ways, Scott rejected Marxism along with virtually any
political analysis or ideology. Whether Marx or Adam Smith, Scott
believed the onset of the technological age had rendered such
visions as anachronistic.

He used the example of America's industrial war effort in the early
1940's to note:

> *"The smaller plants can produce several times what the old-
> fashioned plant did, so that instead of regional planned
> industrial area expanding hugely, the area shrinks on them.
> Now,
> besides that, it reduces the capital payoff time. Something
> Karl
> Marx never knew or economists never envisioned. For
> thousands of
> years, the time necessary to pay off the interest and principa*

on a large amortized investment was usually bonded issues with a
hundred years to pay. Well, it took that length of time to pay off. The introduction of energy and technology has reduced it toward zero, and reducing the man-hours toward zero and the
energy consumed per unit produced tends to go down, etc. While
the unemployed tends to rise and unused area tends to rise, or
increase, the production will rise and your available capital Rises." (THSS p. 304)

Technological Innovation vs Outdated Social Mechanisms

For Scott, molding human society and behavior into a utopian state of efficiency and right behavior was a matter of technological design.

In an early interview, he pointed out that the dangerous practice of people hitching rides on car running boards had been solved not by laws or fines, but when manufacturers stopped including running boards in car designs.

It's easy to see how Scott might well approve of something like China's (and the West's quickly materializing) social credit score system, and the "surveillance and service" visions of smart cities.

But he might also have appreciated things like Decentralized Autonomous Organizations (DAOs), and crypto "smart contract" technology which can automate and ensure input and output decision-making according to code.

Scott believed that technology would disrupt and displace every other institution and mode of influence in society.

Along the way, it would displace humans as work units, like it or not:

"America stands now at the crossroads, confronting the dilemma of alternatives. The progression of a modern industrial social mechanism is unidirectional and irreversible. Physically this continental area has no choice but to proceed with the further elimination of toil through the substitution of energy for man hours. There can be no question of returning to pre machine or pre technological ways of life; a progression once started must continue. Retrogressive evolution does not exist." (THSS, p. 26)

Robotics and AI at this stage are encroaching virtually every sector, impinging on formerly human livelihoods. Doling out a "basic income" to aid people lacking higher level skills, has been one proposed answer to the problem.

But most people have not seen their own lives made more leisurely in a highly technological world. If anything, average people with decent education and initiative are working harder and longer, while losing ground in terms of physical wealth, including property, housing and even basics like food and energy.

How might Scott explain it? Actually, he did. Even in the midst of the Depression, he contended that the creation of poverty and want of the time had nothing to do with the industrial or technological capacity of the nation.

He laid the problem at the feet of a warped system of politics and finance.

Scott tagged rampant government debt creation, spiraling taxation and concentration of wealth in corporate entities as being inevitable consequences of an antiquated system of valuation and reward, not a problem of overall productivity.

Perhaps the following passage from 1935 brings to mind some current trends:

"Technocracy's [Scott's magazine / movement] analysis of the national income shows that there are over [77] million families in the United States, comprising in excess of [180] million human beings, who are dependent upon an income of less than $40.00 per week per family; or, as the Brookings Institute puts it, 1/10 of 1 percent of the families at the top receive as much income as 42 percent of the families at the bottom of the national income scale.

"It is self-evident that with a larger and larger proportion of our national income being required to bolster the debt structure and to pay government expenses, the rising prices and the cost of living will lower the consuming power of at least 80 million Americans. Life cannot 'begin' for these Americans—all that is left is subsistence of a low order." (THSS p. 33)

As Gerald Celente might say, it represented "a rigged system."

Scott opined:

"Technocracy has pointed out that a national parade of the dumb, the halt, the lame, and the blind was about to begin. That national parade is on in full swing. We have nationalized Tammany's New Deal, the California Epic Program, old-age pension plans, pleas for social justice, and cries to share the wealth. America might just as well make up its mind that it cannot have economic planning, social justice or guaranteed security under the dominance of a Price System.

"The political administration of our national affairs is deemed by Technocracy to be totally inadequate and incompetent, irrespective of which political racketeer does the administering. Politics and the financial racketeering of the Price System are blood brothers conceived in the ages of scarcity along with the oxcart, the sickle, the hoe, and the spade; and, like them, they have become as obsolete and must be consigned to historical antiquity." (THSS p. 33)

Scott believed the financial system of assigning debt to almost exponentially accelerating productivity, was stratifying haves and have-nots, and enriching corporate entities to the detriment of overall human benefit:

"Our forefathers in attempting to guarantee to future Americans life, liberty, and the pursuit of happiness, placed their hope of fulfillment in political liberty and reckoned not that the day would arrive when the interference control of the Price System would conflict with the development of technology—that America would be compelled to make the rich richer and the poor poorer...

"Our national leaders of the past two decades have always proclaimed the inherent soundness of the Price System. Their voices have always been raised in defending and boosting their own America. Their America was a glorious hunting ground where private corporate enterprise was permitted the privilege of creating debt claims against others faster than they were created against them. It was heads I win, tails you lose; no one else could possibly win. Every consumer was a sucker, legitimate prey for the corporate enterprise of yesterday and today." (THSS, pg 38-39)

Another evil of America's reliance on distorted incentives of production for the outsized profit of a relative few, and currency-manipulated finance and banking, was the requisite need to sell to the world.

Scott believed that areas of the world naturally bound by geography should focus on "continental" and not global betterment. It was effectively a "North America Continent First" philosophy. In the wake of WWII in 1947 he opined:

> *"Under a Technate, we would have no interest in sending our troops or our warships to finagle some foreign territory for the benefit of a bunch of American chiselers. We would make this continent the finest place in the world to live, and the rest of the world could learn from our example here.*

> *"We would export methods and specifications of continental operation that would be worth something to the world instead of the dollar diplomacy and the dollar goods that we're trying to shove down the throats of the Chinese, the Romanian, the Italians, and the French or anybody else".* (THSS p. 508)

By the 1960's, Scott was issuing more dire warnings about the worsening effects of America's bloated domestic tax and governing system, and foreign economic strategies and subsidies:

> *"The time is running out for this system of ours. We have over 16,000 municipalities and 17,000 townships in the United States, and a little less than 100,000 total governments that are empowered to levy taxes and collect them and to issue debentures. In other words, there has been no major change in the structural operation of the United States in 180 years. Our structure is obsolescent and antique. It is incompetent to take care of the imperatives of this modern world of our day. So, what? We have done some marvelous things in many ways. We've put in installment buying, we've promoted this, we recovered Germany after*

World War I with the Young Plan and the Dawes Plan and after World War II the Marshall Plan, bolstered up every economy in Europe and some not in Europe. Well, now they're all bolstered up with a lot of new technological equipment and capacities beyond that they ever dreamed of...

"...Marvelous! This kind of game is about running out. The total debt in the United States just announced is 1.4 trillion. It's increased enormously in the last seven years. The interest on the federal debt this year—that's interest payments—will exceed $15 billion. That's a sizable chunk. The total budget of the United States didn't reach that for more than a century and a half. Well, now we're stuck with it." (THSS p. 1888-89)

The Decline of the Technical Alliance?

Though Scott believed that politically agnostic technocrats were best suited to employing science to solve the growing imbalance of productive abilities and innovations, and the equitable distribution of wealth created, his organization never attempted to politically organize.

That's because Scott both despised the workings of politics, and believed the eventual assumption of power of technocrats was inevitable, though humankind might stupidly delay in evolving.

The Technical Alliance grew in number until the late 1940's, when Scott's controversial views regarding WWII and other other matters caused his organization to ebb.

Even in his latter years, Scott refused to advocate for any political movement to spur on a Technocracy.

In a broad sense, since Scott's death in 1970, the world has proceeded substantially in a direction that he outlined, at least in terms of the ascendancy of technocrats. Today, technocrats dominate society to an unprecedented degree.

They are hardly the disinterested Spock-like characters Scott promised, of course.

Bill Gates, Anthony Fauci, Mark Zuckerberg, Jeff Bezos, Ray Kurzweil, CRISPR gene editing technology co-creator Jennifer Doudna and others may exude a scientific aura in their pronouncements and agendas. But many leading technocrats have been shown to be as subject to megalomania and corruption as any politician, king or religious leader ever was.

Many of them also have long histories of political manipulation to further their own power and objectives. The science-based objectivity that Scott ascribed to technocrats as a class was one of his most persistent and naive conceptions.

As for the ultimate technocrat perhaps being a transhuman or non-human intelligence ala the visions of evangelists like Ray Kurzweil, Scott might well have favored such a development.

But it might be that "consciousness" and self-awareness themselves introduce a will that is subject to temptations of power and evil. In that case, so much for Technocracy as heaven and technocrat—human or otherwise—as benevolent gods.

SAGE OF THE TECHNOCRATIC MINDSET: THOMAS SOWELL

(first published 23 Mar 2021 in the *Trends Journal*)

The technocratic mindset is not defined by a hubris that a privileged or elite group or class can better decide the course of human "progress" than the relatively freely chosen interactions and choices of billions of the world's inhabitants.

The notion is not particularly new. In some ways it's as old as mankind, and rooted ultimately in a dark facet of human nature which desires power over others.

Before there were "technocratic" elites, relying on predictive modeling and analytics of AI and super computers and information networks, there were "rational" elitists. And before that, there were "Sun Kings", closer to the gods and therefore more deserving of decision-making power and status.

The economist and political philosopher Thomas Sowell identified the latter as a kind of organic meta "intelligence". It can be seen in the economic performance of free markets vs. directed economies. It can also be evidenced in the quality of civic life of free societies vs. totalitarian regimes.

Sowell described the characteristic pattern for the way elites acquire a political mandate for controlling and directing society, and carry out their agenda. His insights are all the more prescient, considering how the COVID pandemic has played out. Sowell named four typical stages of elite intervention:

- Stage 1: "The Crisis"
- Stage 2: "The Solution"
- Stage 3: "The Results"
- Stage 4: "The Response"

The "Crisis" stage is an opportunity never to be wasted, to further the aims of the technocratic elites. A crisis can be a chance or unforeseen occurrence that can be exploited. Think of a sensational video appearing to show a black man being suffocated with a knee on the neck by a white police officer. Or a crisis can be something brought into public awareness via a steady, coordinated effort of organizations and interests with something to gain by changes to policies. Think "climate change".

The "Solution" stage is where elites, have defined the crisis and achieved a certain level of public acquiesce, roll out desired policies, which often have only the most tangential relationship to the actual "crisis". Consider the Federal Government's latest 1.9 Trillion dollar "COVID" relief spending spree.

The "Results" stage is where policies instituted by elites, while empowering and enriching favored entities, have usually very obviously failed in successfully smiting the original "Crisis". Think vaccines, and the eventual, inevitable news that protection conferred is ephemeral.

The "Response" is when elites use the very failure of their policies as a reason to double down on further policies to combat the ongoing, interminable "crisis". Think "more COVID vaccinations", or future lockdowns to combat global climate change, which precipitated the easy spread of the COVID virus, etc. etc.

Limits of the Technocratically "Enlightened"

Sowell's essential point is that no group of oligarchs, however "enlightened", will ultimately make disinterested decisions. Given enormous power, they will be corrupted by that power, according to very infallible human nature.

And even if they could act dispassionately, the "mass intelligence" of millions of relatively free people interacting and making compacts with each other will always outperform the proscriptions of a few "wise" elites.

One could argue that Sowell's analysis did not foresee the capabilities of supercomputers and modeling to capture and synthesize vast amounts of data.

But even if the capabilities approached the meta-understanding of the "mass human intelligence" Sowell described, the concentration of power in the hands of a few humans would still be the point of failure.

And in the hands of an artificial intelligence? As envisioned in many dystopian novels and movies, as well as by some people currently working in the upper echelons of tech giants, the results might be even more catastrophic.

AMAZON USING DIGITAL BOOK DOMINANCE TO CENSOR

(first published on 16 Mar 2021 in the *Trends Journal*)

It seems every week some aspect of a classic dystopian novel jumps off the page and into the designs of the Technocracy. This week, two congressmen were shining a spotlight on Amazon's bolder moves into censoring books.

Why does it matter? Because over the last decade, the tech behemoth has gained a de facto monopoly in digital bookselling and reading, thanks to its Kindle eBook ecosystem.

> *"Big Tech, including Amazon, is engaged in systematic viewpoint-based discrimination. In the unfortunate phenomenon of 'cancel culture,' Amazon plays a leading role in silencing and censoring the political speech of conservative Americans."*

Those objections by Reps. Jim Jordan and Ken Buck were part of a letter to Amazon CEO Jeff Bezos, requesting the company turn over any documents and information related to its alleged censorship activities.

Jordan is the top Republican on the House Judiciary Committee, while Buck is a ranking member of the Subcommittee on Antitrust.

The letter noted that Amazon has been stepping up a pattern of censorship over the past year, targeting books and authors that have conservative viewpoints.

"Innovative" Technology Designed to Monopolize

Amazon's model of "publishing" has operated much like its system of product selling. On the front end, it developed an ultra-easy platform for consumers to find and compare low-cost products and content, complete with user reviews about quality and satisfaction. On the back end, Amazon created a vendor system that made it easier to sell, with Amazon taking its cut.

But at the same time Amazon was "helping" consumers and vendors, it was gradually offering a wider selection of its products, competing with vendors. The company's privileged access to its own data gave them a competitive edge in sourcing, pricing, and analytics, allowing them to win a rigged game of "competition."

Many vendors have been left in an impossible situation. They have to sell on Amazon or at least try since it now commands a huge segment of online buying. But competing with the behemoth that holds all the digital cards means vendors are selling on razor-thin margins, while progressively losing market share to the very competitor they're forced to support.

The same has increasingly been true for book publishers and authors. Peter Hildick-Smith of the research firm Codex Group has noted that Amazon Publishing operates not so much as a traditional publisher, but as a content creator feeding a subscription machine. Their low-priced and even "free books" that come with subscriptions have put a death squeeze on traditional publishers.

A Free Hand to Censor

Amazon has also forced authors to sell their books exclusively on their platform, to be eligible for Kindle Unlimited revenues. Such moves, and not just technical innovations, have allowed the company to increasingly dominate, via a system where most authors make very little, while the tech giant profits from an ever-growing digital "library" of content.

Janet Freidman, a long-time publishing industry professional who puts out the influential "Hot Sheet" newsletter for authors, says Amazon Prime and Kindle Unlimited now earn close to $6 billion for Amazon.

> *"It might be wise to think of Amazon Publishing as a Netflix or Spotify. Amazon Prime members look to Kindle First, Prime Reading, and the Kindle Owners Lending Library for free ebooks to maximize their subscription value; Kindle Unlimited subscribers who pay a monthly fee for access may rarely venture outside Amazon's selection."*

Having corned the bookselling market, Amazon has become increasingly free to censor content without worrying about opening a door to competition. Notably, while Jeff Bezos's net worth literally doubled during the pandemic lockdowns of 2020, Amazon Kindle has refused to publish certain books challenging the efficacy of the COVID lockdowns.

Amazon has also censored its other services. Its cloud storage platform cut off service to the social media platform Parler at a critical moment during post-election allegations of voting fraud in Democrat-controlled urban precincts in a handful of key battleground states.

TECHNOCRATS WIDEN WEALTH GAP THANKS TO PANDEMIC

(first published on 13 Apr 2021 in the *Trends Journal*)

While average Americans were clamped in lockdown for most of 2020, losing their small businesses, or laid off or let go from jobs, waiting on meager government checks, the elites were profiting.

How much? An April 6th article in *The Washington Post* detailed some of the divide. As a class, billionaires more than doubled their net worth, with technocrats like Jeff Bezons, and Elon Musk leading the way.

That's right. While the GDP was taking a nosedive to minus 33 percent, billionaires were growing their coffers at rates not seen since the heady days of the railroad tycoons of over a century ago.

America led the way in shifting wealth to billionaires and minting new ones. But China was close behind. Overall, 2,755 billionaires the world over added about $8 trillion to their total net worth, according to the *Post*, and now account for 13.1 trillion in wealth.

The "Billionaires Club" grew by a third, which means that though newcomers did well, the established members did even better.

Adding insult to injury, many of those same elites obscenely profiting off the pandemic have managed to burnish their images as noble contributors to pandemic and other relief efforts. Amazon commercials have boasted about relatively paltry pandemic contributions.

The Bill and Melinda Gates Foundation, meanwhile, has churned out announcements and articles, including their latest one, "Why We're Giving $250 Million More to Fight Covid-19". The self-congratulation oozing such pronouncements avoids talking about how much Gates and his cronies have made, and how their largesse is a literal drop in the bucket of that wealth:

"Today, the Gates Foundation is making its largest single contribution to fight the pandemic—$250 million. Why so much? And why now? It's been roughly a year since COVID-19 first appeared…"

The Foundation boasts that it has given a total of $1.75 billion to pandemic efforts. But as the article alludes to, much of that "philanthropy" is actually vaccine infrastructure development in nations around the world. Think of it as seed money that yields huge profits for pharmaceuticals, when they charge governments billions for vaccine doses that get distributed.

Of course, poorer countries are getting subsidized vaccines, contributed by EU nations, and the U.S. But the profiteers of Big Pharma, including Gates, are getting paid huge sums for vaccines that are outright mandatory in some countries, and heavily promoted and propagandized for virtually everywhere else.

And so it has been with most of the COVID agenda, including enforced lockdowns. Real world data has shown that lockdowns have done nothing to stem the spread of the virus. Just as data shows that the vast majority of people receiving vaccinations have next to no risk of serious consequences from the COVID virus.

But those lockdowns and urgent vaccine programs are serving a purpose, as clear and the black and red on an old ledger sheet.

Amazon "The Only Game In Town"

Ironically, the Jeff Bezos owned Amazon, which arguably made the most off the pandemic, declined comment for the Bezos' owned *Post* story.

"Amazon had a phenomenal year, from a financial perspective," said Morningstar equity research analyst Dan Romanoff. "They are pretty much the only game in town."

The company increased their total share of e-commerce to a staggering 42 percent, as locked-down consumers were forced to do much of their shopping online.

Amazon's revenue grew nearly 38 percent in 2020. Its current market capitalization of $1.6 trillion tops the entire current value of all the Bitcoin ever minted, which is saying something.

But Amazon has hardly been alone. Other online retailers like Walmart have seen watershed profits, and so have big chain restaurants and tech companies that facilitate functioning in the "new normal" of virtual meetings, virtual purchases, virtual entertainment, and virtual life.

Little wonder that those same entities and personages making huge profits have mostly prosetilized for and funded efforts, campaigns and radical societal changes that have benefited their bottom line.

PORTALS OF POWER: HOW MEGA BILLIONAIRES USURP ELECTIVE BODIES

(first published on 11 May 2021 in the *Trends Journal*)

Billionaire elites continue to pour money into a system of extra-government organizations bent on co-opting power from voters and democratic institutions. One example is a joint portal system run by the Open Society Institute World Economic Forum (WEF).

Two of the world's most powerful billionaires, George Soros and Klaus Schwab, employ the portal system to sign up companies and government agency decision-makers to connect and work out their elite-friendly policies and objectives.

The WEF website hosts a page that promotes the joint effort with the Open Society Institute. There are links to several "big picture" platforms, each overseeing a stunning number of specific projects, all seeded by a combination of billionaire, corporate, and government funding. The portals allow corporate and government reps to sign on and "participate" in the projects.

Projects have a laser focus on controlling virtually all of the most fundamental components of human activity. There are multiple projects designed to establish greater elitist control over food, energy, land, water, transportation, means of exchange (money including digital currencies and decentralized cryptos), technology, and, of course, information and political power.

The WEF admits that it is usurping the power of electoral bodies. Consider, for instance, the overview statement on the portal dedicated to "Shaping The Future Of Public Goods":

> *"Government alone cannot deliver on the global UN Sustainable Development Goals or the Paris Agreement on*

179

climate change. Our Platform enables leaders from the public and private sectors and civil society worldwide to form exceptional, cross-cutting communities of action that collaborate at speed and scale, harness the opportunities of the Fourth Industrial Revolution and trigger systems change.'

Soros, Schwab, and other mega-billionaires like Bill Gates have gone far beyond what the old wave of 19th and 20th-century industrialists fomented with organizations like the Rockefeller and Carnegie foundations. In fact, many old-line organizations have fallen completely in line with globalist objectives to concentrate power and remove any meaningful policy control from average citizens.

The views and perspectives of voters are not respected. Various initiatives with "woke" sounding labels seek to manipulate and control debate and votes as completely as the control sought over food, energy, or technology.

A Listing of Some of the Open Society/WEF Joint Projects

The following outline list gives an idea of some of the portals and sub-projects (with parenthetical decoding of project objectives):

- Shaping the Future of Global Public Goods
    - Net Zero Carbon Cities / The Net Zero Challenge / Mission Possible Partnership / (changing how and what energy resources we're allowed to use under the rubric of "net-zero" carbon goals, etc.)
    - Food Innovation Hubs / The Future Of Protein / Incentivising Food Systems Transformation / Food Systems Initiative (focused on controlling food resources and eliminating meat consumption)

- o Global Water Initiative / 2030 Water Resources Group (wresting control of water rights from private landowners)
- o Nature Action Agenda /
- o Lighthouse Projects on Social Justice and Sustainability / Technology and Social Justice Community (compelling the adoption of leftist woke agendas including BLM and LBTQ into corporate and governmental institutions)
- o Deep Sea Minerals Dialogue (controlling natural resources even in open waters)

- Shaping the Future of the New Economy and Society
  - o Closing the Gender Gap Accelerators / Hardwiring Gender Parity in the Future of Work (requiring "gender parity" in all hiring)
  - o Partnering for Racial Justice in Business (positing "systemic racism" as fact and promoting discriminatory policies to advantage targeted racial groups)
  - o Partnership for Global LGBTI Equality (PGLE)

Besides the specific partnership platforms of the WEF and Open Society, the WEF also funds a considerable number of other platforms seeking to shape the future of CyberSecurity, Consumption, Financial and Monetary Systems, and much more.

A Funded Wonderland Of Hypocrisy, Elitism, and Radical Agendas

Even projects that appear to have good intentions are often cluelessly un-self-aware and hypocritical. Consider the project promulgating "Circular Electronics." The idea is that the electronics industry processes and materials should be designed and geared as much as possible to reuse and reclaim.

It sounds laudable unless a moment is spent meditating on how the same corporations advocating "Circular Electronics" force-feed new versions of software and hardware devices. Google Chromebooks, for example, have built-in expiration dates, beyond which they stop receiving security updates, rendering them vulnerable, though they still function perfectly well otherwise.

And how many average computer or cell phone users can cite a five- or ten-year-old program they used that had more functionality than a newer operating system or app?

It's an old game that was played 50 years ago with cars and TV sets. Only today, corporations create social pressure to acquire the "latest and greatest" through insidiously pervasive social media and advertising control. All while preening about their social responsibility and initiatives like "circular electronics."

Unsurprisingly, among the experts who advise and develop the agendas and proscriptions of the projects are many hardened leftists in academia, government, media, and globalist corporations.

A perusal of the persons and agendas shows just how specific and granular are the control aspirations and mechanisms of two of the world's most influential globalist organizations.

BUYING AMERICA'S NEWSROOMS

(First published on 18 May 2021 in the *Trends Journal*)

"Report For America", an organization that subsidizes the hiring of selected reporters at regional and local newspaper outlets, recently announced an expanded initiative. A new "Report For The World" program has been launched to place journalists in newsrooms in Africa and other nations.

Since 2017, Facebook and Google, among other left-leaning funders, have used "Report For America", which is administered under the auspices of the "The Ground Truth Project", to build influence over the hiring of and development of "social justice" reporters. In 2021, the program placed 300 reporters across the U.S.

And their goals over the next few years are even more ambitious: "Next year, we'll send even more reporters throughout the country," their website boasts. "We aim to place 1,000 reporters by 2024 and strive to fundamentally transform local news business models and ecosystems."

The way the project works is straightforward. Newsrooms can apply in a "competition", by outlining "urgent gaps in coverage" and specifying how they will use reporters. Winning newsrooms are supplied with a reporter whose salary is half-subsidized by the RFA.

Aspiring journalists can apply to be part of the program. "The Report for America corps members get world class training, at the beginning of the term and throughout the service years. The term is one year with an option for a second year (most corps members end up serving two years)."

What say do local news organizations have in choosing reporters they want? Not much. "Report For America" controls what journalists are accepted into their program. And local newsrooms can only choose from a small selection of Report For America's "pre-screened candidates":

> *"RFA will screen the large pool of talented applicants and choose three to five well qualified candidates to present to the local news organization. You make the final selection."*

A Brief Survey Of Reporter Projects

RFA has a page listing reporting projects of journalists funded by their program. It reads like a litany of "social justice" and "critical race theory" in action. Some recent examples of RFA journalist reporting include:

- WFAE - Race and equity beat
- City Limits - Climate change and its implications for New York City
- Sahan Journal - Immigration policy especially affecting the Hmong Somali and Latino communities
- The Public's Radio - Race and poverty in Newport R.I.
- DCist - Photojournalism involving minority communities in Wards 7 and 8 in D.C.
- Associated Press, OH - Ohio legislature, especially related to abortion, gun control and opioid settlements
- The Akron Beacon Journal - Minority and immigrant issues
- The Mercury News - Economic inequality in San Jose and for The California Divide Project
- The Charlotte Observer - Status of poor and minority communities in a prosperous city
- Mission Local - Inequality and income disparities in Mission District of SF

- The News & Observer - Minority communities in North Carolina
- The News Tribune, in partnership with The Olympian, The Bellingham Herald, and The Tri-City Herald - Indigenous communities in Washington State
- Henrico Citizen - Educational equity in Henrico County, VA
- The Community Voice - Criminal justice system and African-American community in Kansas
- The Columbus Dispatch - Bhutanese and other immigrant communities in central Ohio
- The Haitian Times - Community coverage of Little Haiti in Miami
- Traverse City Record-Eagle - Indigenous communities in Northern Michigan
- Associated Press TEXAS - State legislature and the politics of climate change
- The Texas Observer - Indigenous tribes in Texas as part of a new Indigenous Affairs team
- The Plug - Innovation and start-up initiatives at Historically Black Colleges and Universities
- IndyStar - Education, health and business issues and gaps in African-American and Latino communities

RFA notes that it is not open to "advocacy journalism" outfits. But their goal isn't to seed groups already aligned with their ideological agenda. Their aim is to "fundamentally transform" local newsrooms that may not yet be wholly subverted by the hardline leftist lenses of social justice and critical race theory.

RFA: Deep Ties to Democrat Political Machines and Leftist Media

Report For America was co-founded by Steven Waldman and Charles Sennott. Both men have organizing backgrounds, and deep connections to democrat political machines.

Waldman served as senior advisor to the CEO of the Corporation for National Service, the government agency in charge of former President Bill Clinton's own political seeding "AmeriCorps" initiative.

Studies have shown AmeriCorp has been successful in grooming participants for government jobs. Waldman also served as a senior advisor to the FCC during the Obama administration. His brother Michael Waldman was Clinton's White House Director of Speechwriting, and now serves as president of the Brennan Center for Justice at NYU's School of Law.

Waldman wrote a report in 2015, "Report for America", which called for a national program to "improve local journalism". He ended up teaming with Charles Sennott, founder of The Groundtruth Project, to make it happen.

Charles Sennott's bio includes working for PBS Frontline and NewsHour, as well contributing for MSNBC, CNN and the BBC. Before that, he reported for the Daily News and the Boston Globe. If that's not enough clue where his politics lie, his columns available here should leave no doubt.

News For America is another example of how corporate powers and foundation billionaires operate at a practical level, funding experienced political organizers and groups to seed institutions with loyal zealots.

NFA Funders: A Who's Who of Global Corps and Fellow-Traveling Foundations

As mentioned, Facebook and Google are major funders of NFA. The "Facebook Journalism Project" has contributed $4.5 million, and Google added $400 thousand. Big tech companies already wield vast control over internet information, via search engines, social media ecosystems and closed hardware and software systems and app stores.

But especially since 2016, Google, Facebook, Apple, Amazon and Twitter have established more specific control and manipulation of news organizations. NFA is part of that.

BILLIONAIRE TAX SCOFFLAWS PLOW SAVINGS INTO WEBS OF CONTROL

(first published on 15 Jun 2021 in the *Trends Journal*)

Just how are the rich getting richer?

The COVID pandemic showed more starkly than ever how mega billionaires like Jeff Bezos, Bill Gates, Laurene Powell Jobs, Klaus Scwhaab and others can profit even more from disasters than from good times.

Did they merely provide goods and services more creatively and ingeniously than competitors?

The web of activist organizations and entities fueled by their foundations is prolific. They wield influence in virtually every area: culture, commerce, news, education, health, and of course, politics.

Are they merely exercising their rights to dispose of their wealth as they see fit?

The very obvious, non-conspiratorial answer is no. Their networks exert tremendous, corrosive influence that has siphoned power from localities, average voters and even national politicians and governments. It's not an exaggeration to say that at this point, globalist technocratic elites have effectively turned Western democracies into slavish zombie states.

"Rigged System" doesn't even begin to describe it

A new in-depth report by non-profit news organization ProPublica details how some of America's wealthiest activists engage in obscene tax avoidance schemes. The record shows that in years when they have paid a relative pittance in taxes, they have funded activist causes by the billions.

Incredibly, a lot of the richest names list also made another list: "Years In Which a Billionaire Paid No Personal Income Taxes". Names there include:

- Jeff Bezos (2007 and 2011)
- Elon Musk (2018)
- Michael Bloomberg
- Carl Icahn (2016 and 2017)
- George Soros (2016, 2017, 2018)

George Soros represents a typical example of how tax laws have been met with creative impunity by elites. The activist billionaire and naturalized American citizen managed to claim losses from 2016 to 2018, despite a generally good U.S. economy and rising stock market.

At the exact same time, Soros infused his Open Society Foundation, the umbrella funder of his left-wing activism, with 18 billion dollars. *The New York Times* called it "one of the largest transfers of wealth ever made by a private donor to a single foundation."

Soros money funded the "Resistance" to Donald Trump, undermining his Presidency with now discredited claims of "Russian collusion". And in 2018 Soros began a program funneling millions to campaigning leftist district attorney campaigns around the country, to steer criminal justice policies.

"True Tax" shows how much the richest are benefiting

Tax avoidance is accomplished in a myriad of ways. As an example, Carl Ichan, claimed interest off huge loans that were being leveraged to finance investments in 2016 and 2017. That helped him in claiming no Federal tax liability for several years, despite $544 million in adjusted gross income.

Michael Bloomberg could thank rival Donald Trump in part for his 2018 tax avoidance success. On $1.9 in reported income he used Trump era tax cuts, together with charitable donations and credits for foreign taxes paid, to drastically reduce his domestic tax bill.

In addition to zero tax years, mega-millionaires have managed to generally pay rates of tax that would be the envy of average Americans employed as teachers, office workers, healthcare technicians and first responders. Unlike average working Americans, much of the wealth growth of the mega rich is not gained via "salaries".

The ProPublica analysis devised a way to illustrate how tax laws allow the wealthy to escape the percentages that average Americans pay. They compared how much in taxes the 25 richest paid each year, to how much their estimated wealth grew over the same time period. ProPublica dubbed that their "true tax rate".

In the years 2014 to 2018, the richest 25 gained $400 billion in wealth, and paid around 13 billion in taxes. Their true tax rate over that period? 3.4 percent. Some marquee names paid the least:

- Warren Buffett: .10 percent
- Jeff Bezos: .98 percent
- Michael Bloomberg: 1.30 percent
- Elon Musk: 3.27 percent

In contrast, middle class Americans who saw their net worth expand by about 65-thousand during the 2014 to 2018 time frame, paid about $62 thousand in taxes over that same period.

During the COVID War, the wealth bonanza only grew more grotesque. **Trends Journal** articles including TECHNOCRATS WIDEN WEALTH GAP THANKS TO PANDEMIC (13 Apr 2021) summarized how the elites got richer while the rest of the world suffered in 2020.

The ProPublica report is causing a stir, due to the fact that the reporting is based on a leak of IRS documents. According to *Wikipedia*:

> *"IRS Commissioner Charles Rettig said that the IRS would investigate the leak of the tax data to ProPublica and that any violations of law would be prosecuted."*

Though a frankly activist outlet itself, ProPublica has shown more balance than many other millionaire-funded journalistic projects. In 2013, for example, they covered the story of how the IRS illegally targeted and held-up the applications for tax exempt organizations with conservative leanings. They've earned five Pulizers since their founding in 2007.

Their stated mission to expose abuses of power and betrayals of the public trust has certainly hit pay dirt with their latest report.

"YOU CAN NEVER BE WOKE ENOUGH": HOW ELITES ARE CREATING A DISSOCIATIVE POPULACE

(first published on 22 Jun 2021 by the *Trends Journal*)

How much do facts and logic matter in the current wars radically transforming every aspect and detail of our lives?

Some are arguing not at all, and they may be right.

Technocratic elites are not waging a war of facts. They are engaged in psychological warfare on a scale Americans have never before experienced.

Their object is to attain a level of control where citizens dissociate from their own experience and knowledge, and accept the State and its technocratic "experts" as the sole arbiters of reality.

The psychological war can be seen across many battle fields including:

- The COVID War
- Climate Change
- Critical Race Theory
- Nationalism
- "Equity"
- Sex and Gender
- The Surveillance State
- Decentralized blockchain technologies
- Genome experimentation and transhumanism
- GeoPolitical relations with Russia, China, Israel and others

Cultural observer and author Jay Dyer recently observed that *1984*, the great novel predicting a future totalitarian dystopia, wasn't primarily about the technical innovations by which people would be controlled. The book was a treatise in psychological torture and reprogramming. The object was to bring the protagonist, Winston Smith, to a point where he only accepted as true or real what "Big Brother" (ie. the technocratic state) endorsed as true and real.

In other words, no personal observation, no use of logic, no call to historical veracity or empirical evidence, and no moral or ethical consideration was to be used to assess and understand reality.

Smith was re-educated, via systemic psychological and physical torture, to disassociate from any apprehension of reality apart from what the technocratic state posited as reality, on a day to day, and indeed, moment to moment basis.

The Modern Moment of Dissociative Reality

A dissociative psychological state, where a person feels deadened and detached from their life, their own physical senses, their memories and sense of self, is a noted outcome of sustained brainwashing, imprisonment and torture.

A dissociative break can result when people are pressured or tormented into denying things which they know are true.

In the famous example from *1984*, Winston Smith is tortured until he not only is willing to state that "two plus two equals five", but believes it, though it impossibly contradicts his own obvious apprehension and knowledge.

There are many analogies to "two plus two equals five" being promulgated by technocratic authorities in government and society today. But as important as naming the examples themselves, is calling out the coercive techniques being used to induce people into dissociating from their own knowledge and understanding.

Some of the current social techniques include:

- Ridiculing and ostracizing dissenters in popular culture
- Criminalizing deviations from "right-speak"
- Ghettoizing (ie. separating and punishing) people who stray from orthodoxy or approved behaviors
- Banning dissenters from means of communication
- Subjecting dissenters to loss of employment and schooling opportunities
- Pressuring or forcing public recantations of dissident opinions and statements

Needless to say, the above examples are indications of a radicalization of society, in service of the powers endorsing and carrying out such techniques. In America today, almost all cultural, educational and political and even religious institutions have been co opted into actively using these techniques to coalesce all authority in the technocratic state.

Joe Rogan, an icon known for the most listened to podcast in the world, recently articulated some of the pressures the technocratic state is capable of exerting:

"You can never be woke enough, that's the problem, it keeps going, it keeps going further and further and further down the line. And if you get to the point where you capitulate where you agree to all these demands, it will eventually get to straight white men are not allowed to talk. Because it's your privilege to express yourself when other people of color have been silenced throughout history. It will be you're not allowed to go outside because so many people were imprisoned for so many years.

"I mean, I'm not joking, it really will get there. It's that crazy. You know, we just got to be nice to each other, man. And

there's a lot of people that are taking advantage of this weirdness in our culture, and then that becomes their thing. Their thing is calling people out for their privilege, calling people out for their position. You know, it's so f***ing crazy times."

Rogan has come under increasing censorship and pressure to ban verboten personalities from his show, and to recant his own opinions regarding vaccines, the biological sexes, transgenders competing in sports and more.

Calling out psychological manipulation, and holding those who engage in it to account, is the first step to fighting the war on the right battlefield. No idea, no "reality" worthy of the name should require brute force or social systems of coercion to prevail.

Those who argue "misinformation" requires banning, suppression and de-personing are not only engaged in propaganda. They are the current "woke" thug enforcers of a dissociative state.

A STROLL DOWN 21st CENTURY CONSPIRACY LANE

(First published on 29 Jun 2021 in the *Trends Journal*)

Most conspiracies aren't what they're cracked up to be.

They're not very well hidden. They're usually the overall simplest explanation for what occurred. Even the propaganda efforts pressuring people to discount their own common sense and cognizance of facts don't really qualify as conspiratorial.

John McAfee didn't kill himself. He told us himself in a 2019 tweet, and tattooed it on his arm:

> *"Getting subtle messages from U.S. officials saying, in effect: "We're coming for you McAfee! We're going to kill yourself". I got a tattoo today just in case. If I suicide myself, I didn't. I was whackd. Check my right arm."*

McAfee also explained that there's nothing hidden or "conspiratorial" about the deep state. It's right there, spying on us, and co-opting the powers and undercutting the mandates of our elected representatives.

So, with a nod to McAfee, following is a non-exhaustive perusal of some of the more consequential non-conspiracies of the 21st Century...

The COVID War

COVID-19 was man-made. It was the obvious explanation from the first, and people knew it. MSM rebuttal headlines like "No, the coronavirus wasn't made in a lab. A genetic analysis shows it's from nature" were already making the rounds in March of 2020.

THE COVID WAR, from the virus itself to the implemented "solutions", was a human-created disaster. People know who gained and lost from it. The Chinese and the technocratic elites of the West have been the winners and perpetrators, while the rest of the world lost.

People know wearing masks was never scientific. Neither was social distancing, nor using mad amounts of hand sanitizers. They know lockdowns of "non-essential" local businesses and churches and people, while keeping box chain stories and fast food restaurant chains open, was arbitrary to the point of absurd.

People understand the vaccines are about money, and a test of authoritarian control. They know cheap, safe drugs like Ivermectin and Hydroxychloroquine should have been allowed to be prescribed by doctors, even if efficacy was not proved. For virtually all of 2020, the experimental vaccines weren't even available.

People know COVID "death rates" and "case rates" have been highly manipulated. In the words of Joe Rogan, people claiming otherwise are "saying things they know aren't true. And yet they'll fight for them. There's a weirdness to that."

Chinese Subversion

China is thoroughly embedded in American institutions. It wields power over businesses, and has co-opted our politics.

In 2020, vice dean of Renmin University's School of International Relations Di Dongsheng infamously boasted that the CCP had people "at the top of America's core inner circle of power and influence." He added "we have been utilizing the core power of the United States for the past 30 years, 40 years."

China's infiltration is in the open, on college campuses and schools across the country, in virtually any large business, in entertainment and sports, and, most perniciously, in government. Comprising scandals of China influence involving now President Joe Biden and son Hunter, Senator Diane Feinstein (D-CA), Representative Eric Stalwell (D-FL) and other politicians are not hidden.

China steals hundreds of billions from the U.S. alone in intellectual property, including much cutting-edge technology. They have intercepted data on thousands of American citizens, and have used that information to influence and corrupt decision makers.

Regulatory changes that allowed Obama administration officials to profit off insider deals with China were chronicled in detail in "Secret Empire", a 2018 book by Breitbart editor Peter Schweizer. A Fox Business story at time summarized:

> *"Former President Barack Obama used his executive powers to impose industry regulations that lowered the value of certain companies and led to financial gains for a firm owned by two close family friends, according to Breitbart editor-at-large Peter Schweizer.*

> *"The admissions were revealed in Schweizer's new book, "Secret Empire," which found a pattern of investments in coal, offshore mining and for-profit universities that closely tracked the Obama administration's regulatory policy changes. Billionaire activists Tom Steyer and George Soros were among the beneficiaries."*

Arguably the most significant Chinese "achievements" to date have been mortally wounding the West with a man-made virus, and ousting a President who took the most economic and cultural stance against them in more than 40 years.

Many **Trends Journal** articles have highlighted aspects of China's efforts, including:

- "HIGHEST LEVEL EVER CHINESE DEFECTOR HAS INFO ON WUHAN LAB AND MUCH MORE," 22 June 2021
- "APPLE BETRAYS CHINESE USERS FOR PROFIT," 1 June, 2021
- "AMERICA DRIFTS TOWARD CHINA'S "TECHNO-AUTOCRACY," 9 February, 2021
- "SHAPE OF THE FUTURE: GLOBAL CHINATOWN," 14 February, 2014

The Surveillance State

CNN recently reported on the need for the Federal government and FBI to work more closely with the private sector, in the name of combating "Cyber Crime":

> *"Cybercrime is on the rise throughout the United States, but many of those attacks are not being reported to the authorities, suggests a new report released Sunday by the FBI and the Computer Security Institute (CSI)...*
>
> *"Now, more than ever, the government and private sector need to work together to share information and be more cognitive of information security so that our nation's critical infrastructures are protected from cyberterrorists."*

That "recent" CNN story was from April 2002.

The government has long used "cybersecurity" and "protecting infrastructure" to surveil the American populace. It was there in the Patriot Act, just 45 days after 9/11. As the ACLU has noted:

"Hastily passed 45 days after 9/11 in the name of national security, the Patriot Act was the first of many changes to surveillance laws that made it easier for the government to spy on ordinary Americans by expanding the authority to monitor phone and email communications, collect bank and credit reporting records, and track the activity of innocent Americans on the Internet. While most Americans think it was created to catch terrorists, the Patriot Act actually turns regular citizens into suspects."

In 2013, Eric Snowden confirmed the comprehensive nature and granular details on how it was being accomplished. But the broad outlines were not hidden. Not at all.

The Political Weaponization of Domestic Intelligence

This of course often works in conjunction with the surveillance state. The American political system has been subverted by and via U.S. intelligence agencies.

Intelligence agencies with actors directly connected to the Obama-Biden administration and the 2016 Hillary Clinton campaign hobbled the Trump presidency with spying and knowingly false allegations of "Russian collusion".

The spying, from the summer of 2015 on, was never much of a secret, though Trump and the media warred over the details. By 2020 even NPR was reporting on the undeniable abuses. *USA Today* featured a piece by James Bovard about the sorry state of U.S. domestic intelligence abuses:

"FBI machinations at the FISA court are especially perilous to American democracy because that court is extremely docile to federal agencies. The FISA court 'created a secret body of law giving the National Security Agency the power to

amass vast collections of data on Americans,' The New York Times reported in 2013 after Edward Snowden leaked court decisions. FISA decisions have 'quietly become almost a parallel Supreme Court...regularly assessing broad constitutional questions and establishing important judicial precedents, with almost no public scrutiny.' The court's servility can boggle the imagination, such as its rubber-stamping FBI requests that bizarrely claimed that the telephone records of all Americans were 'relevant' to a terrorism investigation under the Patriot Act, thereby enabling N.S.A. data seizures later denounced by a federal judge as 'almost Orwellian.'

"Ironically, the FISA court was created in 1978 to prevent Nixon-style political spying..."

In 2021, with the Biden administration, the surveillance state has moved on from surveilling the Trump administration, to criminalizing and surveilling his entire support base.

The Financial Manipulators

Financial elites play by special rules, colluding with government to pass off losses, and siphon savings (ie. the fruits of labor) from average Americans. They prey on businesses and whole industries, without regard for country or any greater good. It's not a problem of left vs. right. Occupy Wall Street in 2011, and the 2016 election, with the insurgent campaigns of Bernie Sanders and Donald Trump, were both reactions to it.

In 2007, the only real financial "crisis" was that big banks lost their corrupt leveraged investment and lending casino bets, then demanded the government save them, because doing otherwise would mean a world catastrophe.

In a 12 December, 2007 **Trends Journal** article entitled "Economic 9/11", Gerald Celente laid out the massive scam:

> "Just as the Twin Towers collapsed, from the top down, so too will the US economy from an Economic 9/11. When the high-stakes speculators, banks, brokerages, and buyout firms that leveraged billions with millions get hit ... everything underneath them will turn to rubble.

> "The subprime problem was peanuts compared to the hefty bets made on commercial real estate deals, leverage buyouts, credit spreads, complex mortgage securities, and other esoteric investments that were fabricated with hardly any money down. When the giant firms fall, they'll crush the man on the street."

The culprits were right there, stealing their billions in broad daylight, saddling the public with their losses, and receiving capital infusions instead of jail sentences.

A recent viral podcast featuring Tim Poole with guest Steve Bannon presents a lot of useful perspective on events still playing out from the capitulation to a debt-driven economy rigged to hollow out the working classes.

THE COVID WAR, along with its other "accomplishments", has served as a ready new catastrophe to transfer even more wealth. Meanwhile the masses have again been mollified by reams of stimulus. According to CEIC, an economic analytics firm, United States Total Debt accounted for 895.4 % of the country's GDP in 2020. That represented an all-time high.

9/11

This was the one that started the century off on a footing from which America has never really recovered. Of course, conspiracy theories have famously surrounded the event. But many things concerning 9/11 can't be argued:

- A number of the perpetrators who flew the planes into the World Trade Center were previously known to U.S. Intelligence Agencies, including Mohammad Atta
- The Bush administration whisked Saudia Arabians with connections to terrorist groups out of the U.S. literally as the twin towers smoldered in ruin, with thousands of civilians dead
- The fact that Middle Eastern foreigners were training to fly planes, but unconcerned with learning how to land them, was reported to authorities prior to the attack
- Experts had previously posited that terrorists — the same kind that had hijacked planes throughout the 1970's and '80's — might attempt to fly one into a skyscraper
- Terrorists had already tried to bring down the Twin Towers in 1993, by setting off a bomb in the basement.
- Bill Clinton had declined an opportunity during his Presidency to kill Osama Bin Laden; the "mastermind of 9/11" was later tracked down and killed during the Barack Obama administration

As far as U.S. officials having specific intel on an imminent attack, the official 9/11 Commission Report only determined that there was "vague chatter" surrounding a possible attack.

But people know that a door was left open to the attack. A 2015 documentary The Spymasters, which aired on Showtime in 2015, revealed that the government had much more specific information than the 911 Commission Report allowed.

But was that really surprising? No. The "vague chatter" always sounded like CYA. The revelations of a documentary, dropped in at a safe distance of time, merely confirmed it.

In the documentary, CIA director George Tenet and his chief counter-terror aide, Cofer Black recount receiving information in July of 2001 that was quite a bit more than "vague chatter".

According to Black, the head of the agency's Al Qaeda unit, Richard Blee, informed his superiors that "'Chief, this is it. Roof's fallen in.' The information that we had compiled was absolutely compelling. It was multiple-sourced. And it was sort of the last straw."

Black and Tenet agreed that an urgent meeting at the White House was needed. Tenet said in *The Spymasters* that he picked up the white phone to Condoleezza Rice, President George W. Bush's National Security Adviser:

> *"I said, 'Condi, I have to come see you.' It was one of the rare times in my seven years as director where I said, 'I have to come see you. We're comin' right now. We have to get there.'"*

Tenet recalled the ensuing meeting with Rice at the White House.

> *"Rich [Blee] started by saying, 'There will be significant terrorist attacks against the United States in the coming weeks or months. The attacks will be spectacular. They may be multiple. Al Qaeda's intention is the destruction of the United States.'"*

9/11 set the stage for a new generation of wars and war spending, and much more. The American populace has never been more surveilled and less free than it is as a result of the Patriot Act and many other changes and abuses of U.S. intelligence agencies.

People know that in one way or another, 9/11 didn't have to happen at all. And that's not a conspiracy theory.

HOW BIG TECH MAINTAINS ITS MONOPOLY

(First published on 17 Aug 2021 in the *Trends Journal*)

A handful of Big Tech companies currently control the lion's share of e-commerce, web advertising, social media, cloud services and more. Everyone knows the players: Amazon, Google, Facebook, Apple, Microsoft and Twitter.

They make more the GDP of many countries, escape fair taxation (ie. levels average citizens in many places pay), and manipulate policy debates. They have intimidated and banned opposition, including rival start-up companies, media organizations, and elected representatives such as Senator Rand Paul and former sitting President Donald Trump.

How have these companies maintained their monopolistic abuses of power? One way has been to neutralize competition, by either buying it out or crushing and banning it. Another way has been to inject huge amounts of cash into the campaigns of politicians who protect their interests.

Acquire Or Crush: The Big Tech Response to Competition

Like any oligarchic handful of powers, big tech companies share power among themselves with some competitive jockeying. But they close the club to new players, by either absorbing them before they become economic threats, or crushing them, if their founders refuse the game.

An April 2021 *Washington Post* (owned by Amazon founder Jeff Bezos) story detailed how the largest tech companies have systematically acquired hundreds of companies that might otherwise have upended their lucrative monopolies.

The *Post* referenced a House Judiciary Committee report that called out the dominance and acquisition strategies of some of four major tech companies.

Some of the acquisitions were on public record, but some were not public, or deemed too small to be reported. In other words, Big Tech is constantly buying out innovative emerging companies, and absorbing their innovations long before they can even become threats.

Google purchased small tech companies and their engineers on the way to establishing their Google Apps suite, including Google Docs. Apple made similar small company acquisitions to establish iTunes.

Not all acquisitions have resulted in development. Many are bought out, then left to wither, and are quietly shuttered.

Plenty of acquisitions have involved entities big enough to have made news. For example, the Post noted that Zappos, IMDb, Twitch and Goodreads were all independent companies that Amazon saw as useful or competitive to their media and software empire. They were all snatched up.

Amazon become the "everything store" via billion dollar level buyouts in the good and grocery sphere (eg. Whole Foods), and acquisitions in the electronics and automotive sectors, among others.

Google's acquisition of Motorola Mobility covered its designs on the cellphone space. As far as its lucrative dominating video platform, many people don't even realize that YouTube was once an independent company.

Google Maps in another area where Google dominates, with 80 percent of the market, but not solely via its own in-house wizardry. It notably bought out Waze in 2013, a competitor at the time with a loyal user base.

Concerning Google Maps, Judiciary committee member David N. Cicilline (D-R.I.) commented "[Google] protected that market power, that monopoly power dominance through a series of acquisitions that eliminated any meaningful competitive threat."

Apple's control of music was bolstered by buying out Beats Electronics, which has allowed it to evolve its iTunes music service to compete with Spotify.

Snapchat's story is an interesting case. It began as an app called Picabo in 2011. Its founders, who went to Stanford University, counter-programed against Facebook's idea that people wanted to memorialize their lives in photos forever. The evolving Snapchat app offered photo communications that self-destructed, which appealed to young users unconcerned with leaving something to be remembered by.

Facebook tried to buy out Snapchat in 2013 for three billion dollars, but was rebuffed. So they acquired a rival start-up instead, Instagram, and did everything in their power to promote it to the younger audience. A 2017 MSNBC headline noted: *"Mark Zuckerberg couldn't buy Snapchat years ago, and now he's close to destroying the company."*

That's how the game works. Snapchat has managed to stay independent into 2021, partly thanks to intentional structuring. The company's voting power is distributed between two founders, Evan Spiegel and Bobby Murphy. Despite being publicly traded, the structure means other entities can't acquire enough voting power for a hostile takeover.

But Facebook has also made other successful acquisitions to capture a younger demographic, including the popular messaging service Whatsapp.

Twitter's Jack Dorsey chose to branch out in a novel area, leveraging the success of his micro-blogging platform that has become a defacto standard the world over. He co-founded Square, now a small business payments processing giant centered on mobile phones.

Snuffing Anti-Trust Legislation By Stuffing Campaign Coffers

Just as the largest tech companies have used buy or crush methods to increase and consolidate their dominance of lucrative economic sectors, they have used the same methods to deal with political regulation.

Political forces deemed harmful or unfriendly to their power have not only been suppressed and banned on their platforms and services by the thousands. Tech companies including Google and Facebook have funded efforts to institute mail-in ballot voting changes, secure state house acquiescence, and to control debates over things like net neutrality.

Bill Gates, lacking any medical training or expertise, used his billions to reform his 1990's nadir public image as a predatory capitalist, to become the world's dubious vaccine proselytizer.

Recently Twitter's Jack Dorsey insinuated himself into the crypto provision debate of the Senate trillion dollar infrastructure bill (to be fair, his suggestion was better than what ended up in the bill).

The point is that big tech has increasingly nakedly exercised their power, subverting electoral democracy and Constitutional rights of citizens along the way.

They have amassed armies of lobbyists. Indeed the revolving door between tech companies and U.S. administrations has become a politically incestuous hotbed all its own (see "TECH GIANTS AND NATION STATES: WHO CONTROLS WHO?", 2 Feb 2021).

With all that said, one of the oldest and surest ways to influence politics has also been plied: donating to political campaigns. A recent story by The National Pulse website detailed some of the details. April-June 2021 FEC filings showed Senate Majority leader Chuck Schumer (D-NY) leading the way in funding from big tech:

> *"Over two dozen executives from Microsoft gave over $116,000 combined to the Schumer campaign in June. Among these executives, 13 gave the maximum legally allowed donation, $5,800. Two of the max-out donors were Microsoft President Brad Smith and also Fred Humphries, who leads Microsoft's Washington lobbying team."*

The Pulse noted that Senator Patty Murray (D-Wash.), the third ranking member of the Senate, was given $67,000 from the Amazon PAC and Amazon employees, and $48,000 from Microsoft.

Meanwhile the most aggressive anti-trust legislation introduced in Congress has been opposed by many of the same politicians receiving lucrative donations.

According to the Pulse, California's Silicon Valley has been protected by votes against antitrust measures, cast by Eric Swalwell Zoe Lofgren, and Lou Correa. All those politicians received donations from big tech companies in the run up to votes on the legislation. The National Pulse story can be read here.

The **Trends Journal** has both predicted and chronicled the disturbing evolving reality of Big Tech monopolistic and political power in many previous articles, including:

- "Silicon Valley the new Wall Street?" (20 May 2015)
- 5. Rust Belt 2.0 (4 Dec 2016)
- "Media censorship trend to escalate" (19 Sep 2018)
- "The HI-TECH HEROIN trend" (11 July 2019)
- "CHINA: LEADING THE WAY IN SURVEILLANCE" (11 Dec 2019)
- "FACEBOOK: FU, WE'LL TELL YOU," (6 Oct 2020)
- "FACEBOOK PULLS PLUG ON 'STOP THE STEAL' GROUP" (10 Nov 2020)
- "ALL THE PRESIDENT'S APPS: TECH COUP 2021" (19 Jan 2021)
- "TECH GIANTS AND NATION STATES: WHO CONTROLS WHO?" (2 Feb 2020)
- "FACEBOOK BLOCKS AUSTRALIA NEWS" (23 Feb 2021)
- "AMAZON USING DIGITAL BOOK DOMINANCE TO CENSOR" (16 Mar 2021)
- "TWITTER, FB, APPLE GET A PASS WHILE TEXAS GOV. CONDEMNS GAB" (16 Mar 2021)
- "FACEBOOK EXEC EXPLAINS DYSTOPIAN AI FUTURE" (23 Mar 2021)
- "DHS PARTNERING WITH SOCIAL NETWORKS ON CITIZEN SNOOPING" (13 April 2021)
- "NEXTGOV: WHAT IT IS AND WHY IT MATTERS" (27 Apr 2020)
- "ARE AMERICANS HEADING TOWARD A SILENT SECESSION?" (4 May 2021)
- "TECH GIANTS BIG WINNERS IN PANDEMIC ECONOMY" (4 May 2021)
- AI MIGHT POWER "1984" BY 2024, SAYS MICROSOFT HEAD (1 Jun 2021)

- "BILLIONAIRE TAX SCOFFLAWS PLOW SAVINGS INTO WEBS OF CONTROL" (15 Jun 2021)
- "REUTERS "EXCLUSIVE" CROWS ABOUT BIG TECH MERGING WITH U.S. INTEL TO TARGET POLITICAL DISSIDENTS (27 Jul 2021)
- "SINGULARITY UNIVERSITY: FUELING AI ASCENDANCE" (3 Aug 2021)

HOW BIG TECH MAINTAINS ITS MONOPOLY: A FOLLOW-UP

(First published on 24 Aug 2021 in the *Trends Journal*)

Last week the **Trends Journal** detailed some of the ways Big Tech corporations have propagated their monopolies, in areas including social media, cloud storage and website services, e-commerce, advertising communication, and app development sales and distribution. (See "HOW BIG TECH MAINTAINS ITS MONOPOLY," 17 Aug 2021)

A new guest column by Ken Blackwell at the Townhall website provides more details, specifically concerning how tech corporations have manipulated patent laws and initiatives.

Blackwell, a former Ohio Secretary of State, State Treasurer and mayor of Cincinnati, is currently a Senior Fellow for Family Empowerment with The Family Research Council.

In his column, Blackwell noted that under the guise of "patent reform," big tech lobbyists have consistently pushed for patent law changes that have hurt innovators, and allowed corporations to swallow start-ups on the cheap, and co-opt and even steal technologies, with little risk.

Large tech firms spearheaded the America Invents Act (AIA) of 2011. The legislation increased hurdles for patent holders to get an injunction against a business that was stealing their inventions.

It also established the Patent and Trial Appeals Board (PTAB), which has come to be known as the "patent death squad," for its record of rejecting 80-percent of patent rights claims.

The net effect? Inventors without deep pockets have almost no chance of prevailing in protecting their rights, and corporations can acquire innovations and snuff-out competition for bargain basement prices:

> *"Big companies, particularly big tech, can simply use the patented ideas of others knowing that they will likely get away with it. Even if caught, by the time the process plays out they can simply write a check to a patent holder and have been able to use their technology for years without consequence."*

Judge Paul Michel, former chief judge of the top Federal patent court, has talked about the severe imbalance of power and lack of legal protections that have allowed tech corporations to run roughshod over small start-ups.

Michel pointed out, "powerful tech companies have long relied on a strategy of deliberate infringement because enforcement litigation is too expensive for younger smaller competitors."

Blackwell's column also mentioned how tech companies have lobbied against the STRONGER Patents Act. The bi-partisan legislation has proposed changes to PTAB, and would restore injunctions and protections for property and inventors.

Ken Blackwell's column can be read here.

I'LL TAKE THE VACCINE WHEN...

(First published on 17 Aug 2021 in the *Trends Journal*)

I'll take the vaccine when...

Dr. Anthony Fauci is held in contempt for lying to Congress concerning funding gain-of-function research at the Wuhan lab where COVID-19 likely originated.

I'll take the vaccine when the Director of the National Institute of Allergy and Infectious Diseases is stripped of his position for covering up his role and the role of others in supporting banned and dangerous experiments with viruses.

I'll take the vaccine when Anthony Fauci loses his professional licenses for prohibiting frontline doctors from prescribing safe, cheap medicines on an emergency use basis, at a time when no vaccines for COVID were available.

I'll take the vaccine when Anthony Fauci is stripped of any patent rights to medications or products whatsoever, related to COVID vaccines.

I'll take the vaccine when Anthony Fauci goes to jail for his crimes.

I'll take the vaccine when...

The World Health Organization is disbanded and responsible parties face charges for assisting China in covering up the outbreak and origin of COVID-19.

I'll take the vaccine when China, the U.S. and any other nations found to have conspired or been involved in creating man-made viruses are barred via international agreements from all future experimentation.

I'll take the vaccine when the Centers for Disease Control (CDC) accurately tracks COVID illness and death numbers without distorting and abusing data.

I'll take the vaccine when the CDC accurately and actively pursues the best possible statistical information regarding adverse events from experimental vaccines, and when that information is published and aired regularly by mainstream media.

I'll take the vaccine when institutions charged with the public trust conduct unbiased, peer reviewed studies regarding the efficacy of lockdowns, ventilators, masking, social distancing and other policies that many believe have crippled the nation far more than the virus itself.

I'll take the vaccine when…

Big Tech and Big Pharma relinquish all profits from the COVID pandemic to a fund for people who were prevented from operating their businesses and working at their jobs, and deemed "unessential", while corporations have despicably profiteered to the tune of hundreds of billions.

I'll take the vaccine when vaccine makers, businesses and governments are all subject to individual liability claims for adverse events and harm caused by vaccines.

I'll take the vaccine when corporations that have made trillions promoting unhealthy, fattening products hand over their fortunes to fight obesity, one of the most highly correlated factors in serious COVID illness.

I'll take the vaccine when…

Governors who ordered COVID-positive hospitalized elderly patients back into nursing homes, causing others in that most vulnerable population to become sick and die, meet justice.

I'll take the vaccine when every politician who violated their own COVID edicts resigns and faces enhanced fines and punishments for abusing the public trust.

I'll take the vaccine when elected representatives who violated Constitutionally recognized rights and freedoms of Americans meet the full weight of justice for defying the rule of law.

I'll take the vaccine when…

The flood of illegal immigrants allowed entry in the U.S. during the pandemic, and shuttled around the country, are all sent back to their countries of origin.

I'll take the vaccine when the governmental authorities that have proscribed and enforced restrictions for Americans, while facilitating a illegal immigration crisis, are arrested and face jail for being super spreaders.

I'll take the vaccine when…

Media organizations that promoted overblown fears and false data thoroughly examine all past coverage and issue front page and top of the broadcast corrections.

I'll take the vaccine when media organizations relinquish all the profits they made instilling COVID panic.

I'll take the vaccine when…

Someone explains why forcing people to undergo genetic interventions to deal with manmade scientific maladies sounds like a reasonable idea.

I'll take the vaccine when someone can explain why unprecedented mass violations of Constitutional freedoms are legitimate.

I'll take the vaccine when I believe it's the right medical decision for me, since anything else is a violation of my fundamental human rights.

1984 TO 2021: HOW APPLE LEARNED TO LOVE BIG BROTHER

(First published on 17 Aug 2021 in the *Trends Journal*)

Some are old enough to remember an iconic commercial from 1984, where a woman at a dystopian gathering of prisoners smashes a telescreen screen showing a "Big Brother" like figure.

That commercial was debuted by Apple (during Superbowl 18) to promote its new MacIntosh personal computer.

A narrative voice-over proclaimed "You'll see why 1984 won't be like *1984.*"

At the time, Apple was vying with IBM personal computers and nascent rival Microsoft.

It's surreal enough to contemplate that an upstart computer company would use an evocation Gerorge Orwell's masterpiece of totalitarian oppression to mass market a product, though the year was certainly right for it.

And the commercial made a huge impression.

But the history didn't stop there, unfortunately. Apple has literally evolved to become a major cog in the dystopian present of 2021. Their announcement of "NeuralHash", an initiative that will scan all files in the Apple ecosystem, and report violations to the Government for criminal action, is a culminating step in the growing convergence of a technocracy bent on purging all privacy rights of individuals with respect to the state.

According to *Engineering & Technology* magazine (https://eandt.theiet.org/), the system has supposed limitations built in, but many privacy advocates say NeuralHash is a shocking precedent that opens the door to abuse and deprivations of human rights.

Matthew Green, a John Hopkins University Security Institute said that Apple "has sent a very clear signal. In their opinion, it is safe to build systems that scan users' phones for prohibited content. This will break the dam – governments will demand it from everyone."

The Electronic Frontier Foundation (EFF) also decried NeurahHash, saying it was a "shocking about-face for users who have relied on the company's leadership in privacy and security" while the Center for Democracy and Technology called on Apple to abandon the changes, which it said compromise its guarantee of end-to-end encryption.

As the **Trends Journal** has previously reported in "APPLE BETRAYS CHINESE USERS FOR PROFIT" (1 June 2021), the company has already betrayed its Chinese user base by handing over user iCloud access to Chinese authorities, to cement its opening of a mainland data center in partnership with the state-owned firm Guizhou.

What Does NeuralHash Do?

"NeuralHash," references images from a database provided by child safety organizations to identify known child pornography, and can identify altered images. It reportedly isn't designed to detect fresh child abuse material.

The system can block user attempts to upload an image to its servers. It can also trigger a manual review of suspicious content, send a report to law enforcement, and suspend a user's account.

Apple has stated that NeuralHash would only apply to iCloud Photos, and that no third parties would be able to access or scan images on a user's camera roll.

Constitutional attorney and legal expert Jonathan Turley is warning about the wider privacy abuses of NerualHash and other Big Tech initiatives:

> *"Apple will now use its phones to actively spy on over a billion users to see if any have photos that may be CSAM in order to report them. Imagine the post-privacy world unfolding literally before us. People will have no choice if they have an iPhone in allowing a corporation to monitor their photos. Then, when they use their phones on social media, Twitter and Facebook will censor any views that they object to on subjects ranging from Covid to gender identification to Hunter Biden's laptop to election fraud to even criticism of governments.*

> *"At the same time, the Biden White House has decided that it does not want to deal with the legal or political challenges of seeking to impose a national vaccine mandate. Instead, President Biden has called on corporations to carry out the mandate."*

A Pretext "Key" To Unlock Next Level Surveillance and Suppression

Some might contend that Apple's move is a noble one meant to fight only egregious criminal activities like child exploitation and pedophilia.

But Big Tech, MSM and extremist LBTQT activists have colluded for years in promoting the normalization of sexualized exposure and treatment of children. They have also excused and suppressed organizations that have opposed extremist agendas sexualizing and abusing children.

They have openly advocated not only for exposing children to sexual content, but for allowing children to undergo hormone treatments and deforming cosmetic surgeries to "transition" to the opposite sex. They have also led the way in propagandizing for boys to use girl bathrooms in schools, under the guise of recognizing those who "self-identify" as a particular gender.

To give only a few other examples:

- In 2018, an 11-year-old boy in drag, "Desmond Is Amazing," became a media darling for his sexualized, supposedly personally initiated transexual flamboyance. There were viral Youtube videos, and at one point he even danced on stage at the 3 Dollar Bill, a "queer owned & operated" bar in Brooklyn, and had money tossed his way by patrons. As Lifesite news reported at the time, "[Desmond] is barely 11 years old, yet homosexual and mainstream media have thrust him into the spotlight as the face of the growing prepubescent gay/transgender movement.

- In February 2021, Amazon, Chromebook (by Google), Discord and OnlyFans all made an annual "Dirty Dozen" list of entities that profited from sexual exploitation that encompassed minors. The list is compiled by the National Center on Sexual Exploitation (NCOSE). Amazon reportedly made the list because "the world's titan of e-commerce, logistics, data storage, and media, also peddles endless amounts of sexual exploitation. As a social platform, Amazon's Twitch is rife with sexual harassment, predatory grooming, and child sexual abuse." Twitter was also called out for making the list: "Twitter allows countless posts and accounts that function as advertisements for the trading of child sexual abuse materials (i.e. 'child pornography'), sex trafficking, prostitution, and pornography. Twitter also fails to adequately respond to child abuse and sex trafficking victims when they are being exploited on the platform. Twitter must be held legally accountable".

- Hunter Biden, President Joe Biden's son, was shielded by the MSM during the 2020 election, despite video from an abandoned laptop showing him sexually consorting with underaged women. The media refused to cover the story, with some claiming the laptop was an invention of the Russians. But just last week, new video surfaced from Hunter. It showed him naked, telling a prostitute "the Russians have videos of me doing crazy f-cking sex!" According to a *Daily Mail* story on the unearthed video, Hunter can be seen telling the prostitute that he nearly overdosed from drugs while partying in Las Vegas with his drug dealer and two other guys in the summer of 2018. When he awoke from that bender, "there was this Russian 35-year-old, really nice, pure brunette," he explained. He then discovered his laptop had disappeared.

Clearly, the government, the MSM and Big Tech have been on the bleeding edge of pushing for the sexual exploitation and abuse that Apple suddenly purports to want to guard against.

Anyone who's been paying any attention shouldn't buy a word of the dystopian "product" they're now selling with NeuralHash.

As Jonathan Turley noted in a recent column on his website:

> *"The current limited function of the NeuralHash is simply the decision of Apple. However, it is a new technology that can be expanded to other images and could potentially be used by the government… We already have ample powers to*

investigate and prosecute child pornography but this function will now be taken up by the corporatocracy which is not directly controlled any more by the Fourth Amendment than the First Amendment."

NeuralHash is set to be rolled out later this year as part of updates to Apple's iOS and iPadOS 15.

GOVERNMENT: FREE SPEECH IS BAD FOR YOUR HEALTH

(First published on 21 Sep in the *Trends Journal*)

A Big Tech summit sponsored by Politico last week produced calls for the Federal government to further leverage de facto social communication monopolies to censor Americans.

The summit produced four "top takeaways." But number one on the list targeted free speech rights, via a declaration "Self-Regulation Isn't Going To Cut It":

> *"Facebook and Google have doubled down on efforts to remove misinformation, and more. But, according to lawmakers and advocates, no amount of defensive efforts by the tech industry is going to save companies from impending government intervention."*

Sen. Amy Klobuchar (D-Minn.), one of the attendees of the virtual summit, complained that social networks like Facebook weren't doing enough to promote vaccines. She pointed to a study which she said showed that people who said Facebook was their primary source of news were less likely to be vaccinated.

Klobucher has spear-headed attempts to formalize government control of speech on big tech platforms.

This past July, the Senator introduced The Health Misinformation Act. The bill would create an exemption in the oft-cited Section 230 protections that protect social media companies from liabilities for users posts, since the socials are not considered "publishers."

Klobucher's bill would give the the Department of Health and Human Services (DHHS) new powers over would be considered "health misinformation."

Companies which didn't actively censor user posts and information flagged as health misinformation by the DHHS would be open to liability. In promoting her bill, Klobucher has said:

> *"These are some of the biggest, richest companies in the world and they must do more to prevent the spread of deadly vaccine misinformation. The coronavirus pandemic has shown us how lethal misinformation can be and it is our responsibility to take action."*

Technocratic Censorship Corroding Constitutional Rights

"Health Misinformation" is the term of the moment that social media censors and their allies and overseers in Congress are using to assault free speech protections of American citizens and news companies with dissident views.

The cry has been progressively twisted to censor almost any information and political debate authorities desire to control. For instance, President Joe Biden and Centers for Disease Control (CDC) Director Rochelle Walensky have both recently framed gun ownership as a threat to health rights.

In April 2021, Biden proclaimed the country was in the midst of "a gun violence public health epidemic."

Walensky followed up in August, announcing new CDC efforts to fund research and proscriptions making the case for gun control, though she denied that was the object.
"Climate Change" is another battleground that has been characterized as an urgent public health crisis.

The World Health Organization (WHO) has an extensive list of the health emergencies posed by Climate Change. The CDC, meanwhile, says Climate Change constitutes a significant health threat to the nation and world.

The New England Journal of Medicine has a section of its website devoted to "Climate Crisis and Health." A September 2021 editorial simultaneously published in hundreds of medical journals on the eve of a UN Biodiversity Summit, called for immediate action to reduce global warming, to avoid a health catastrophe.

Migration (supposedly driven by climate change as opposed to corrupt and ineffective government) has been predicated as a health crisis, in studies posted by the National Institute of Health (NIH). The CDC has called "Racism" in America a "serious threat to the public's health."

CDC Director Rochelle Walensky has opined on the CDC's role in combating that crisis: "Confronting the impact of racism will not be easy…I know that we can do this if we work together. I certainly hope you will lean in and join me."

Income Inequality has been called a "healthcare crisis." To give just one recent example, a May 2021 whitepaper by government tied "Project New Dawn," referenced the crisis in outlining the case for establishing a U.S. Central Bank Digital Currency:

> *"Income inequality and associated social divide is causing an irreparable health crisis. Importantly, empirical evidence suggests that the top stressors included money, work, and the economy, with 61% of Americans reporting money as a stressor. Moreover, Americans with lower incomes reported a disproportionately higher amount of stress and higher inability to manage stress (Layte, 2011, Segram and Sequeira, 2020). The extant empirical research supports the notion that lack of financial security leads to both physical and mental ailments."*

Technocratic Censorship Corroding Constitutional Rights

The overall point is not whether firearms, poverty, racism or the weather have health impacts.

The takeaway is that establishing a precedent for Federal authorities to censor "health misinformation," effectively provides power to censor virtually any consequential subject. Anything can be framed as a health issue.

What's more, even the most innocuous, formerly uncontroversial information can suddenly become verboten.

The latest? On Friday, there were reports that Instagram (owned by Facebook), a social media platform favored by a younger demographic, had banned the hashtag #naturalimmunity.

Lackey media outlets spun the news not by disputing the ban, but by saying it risked "fueling conspiracy theorists."

The suppression of different perspectives and relevant facts not only has expanded the power and wealth of a self-serving technocratic class that has repeatedly flouted their own dictates, it has prevented Americans from accessing information and formulating policies that might better their economic and social conditions and their health.

The dynamic has played out with horrendous consequences over the course of the COVID War.

Information on the origins of the virus, U.S. funding of controversial virus experiments, lack of efficacy of lockdowns, masks, social distancing, lack of accuracy of testing and reporting on serious illness and death rates, and efficacy of cheap therapeutics being used with success in other countries, have all been subject to manipulation and censorship serving corporate and governmental agendas.

The **Trends Journal** has been among the leading news sources in the world pointing out those abuses, and compiling a counter-narrative.

At the end of the day, Congress has no constitutional authority to enact legislation of the kind Klobucher advocated at Politico's Tech Summit, which would effectively bar any speech deemed "health misformation."

The First Amendment to The Constitution expressly forbids Congress from restricting free speech:

> *"Congress shall make no law respecting an establishment of religion, or prohibiting the free exercise thereof; or abridging the freedom of speech, or of the press; or the right of the people peaceably to assemble, and to petition the Government for a redress of grievances."*

But the current crop of pols in Congress and state governments aren't proscribing Constitutional rights as a way back to health for the country. They're power-mongers masquerading as medical experts now, pontificating about COVID, vaccines, mask efficacy, the dangers of formerly uncontroversial cheap medicines, and the "health risks" of free speech.

WHY SCIENCE IS THE WORST CULT OF ALL

(First published on 23 Nov 2021 in the _Trends Journal_)

"This attack on me, which clearly has political overtones to a nonpolitical scientist, I feel, is dangerous to the entire field of science and [shows] how people try to intimidate scientists."

—Dr. Anthony Fauci

The quote above came this week, as the head of the U.S. National Institute of Allergy and Infectious Diseases (NAID) defended criticisms over COVID policies and more.

It's not the first time the powerful wielding official has equated himself with "the entire field of science."

Among other things, Fauci was attempting to defend himself regarding anger over his agency funding cruel experiments on dogs.

Typical of the way government agencies have changed documents, studies and definitions to protect narratives, the researchers behind the dog experiments now say NIAID was incorrectly listed as a funder of their study.

But the group that brought the study and its apparent funding to light, the White Coat Waste Project, said they don't believe the revision absolving Fauci.

Spokesman Justin Goodman called the sudden correction, after the story blew up, "too convenient."

Doubling down on the controversy, NIH Director Francis Collins defended his colleague with a threat, demanding that those responsible for criticizing Fauci should be identified and "brought to justice."

"Conspiracies are winning here. Truth is losing. That's a really serious indictment of the way in which our society seems to be traveling," Collins told *The Washington Post*.

Technocrats like Fauci and Collins are wielding dangerous influence and power unconnected with legitimate authority.

They have been allowed to corrupt their role, and have done thereby more than any critics to undermine their own legitimacy.

Science vs. Science Bureaucrats

It must never be forgotten that Science is a method, not an outcome, and certainly not a particular scientist, however influential.

As a method, science limits itself to trying to accurately determine causes and effects, according to observation.

Science is always provisional. It is always subject to revision, based on new advances and discoveries, or rigors of scrutiny.

When scientists advocate, instead of limiting themselves, to rigorously and impartially analyzing, they are stepping beyond science.

It's one thing for public officials or activists to promote policies based on scientific findings.

But when scientists become invested in causes like "Climate Change" or "world-saving" medical interventions, the objectivity necessary for them to carry out their core purpose, is corrupted.

People can root and hope and fight for what they want and believe, based on what they view as faith or fact. But science can't have a dog in any fight, and retain its method, too.

Technocracy as a Cult of Science

The view that technocrats deserve to set policies, and direct the course of human development, ignores the corruption that inevitably results when fact-finders become decision-makers.

Scientists are no more immune to the seductions of power than anyone else.

Increasingly, as scientists have been incentivised to advocate, they have strayed from the limits of their method, to grandiose visions of what can and should be pursued, in the way of the course of human development.

In doing so, science at the present moment has assumed attributes commonly associated with cults.

Try perusing the following list describing typical aspects of cults, while contemplating how the COVID War, climate change policy and "The Great Reset" are currently playing out:

- Cultic organizations, programs, and relationships are built on concerted attempts to persuade and dominate.
- The organization shows an extremely ardent and unquestioning devotion to its leader, and sees his belief system, philosophy, and practices as the Truth, as law (whether he is alive or dead).
- Doubt, disagreement, and questioning are discouraged or even penalized.
- The leadership prescribes how members should think, behave, and feel, often in considerable detail (for example,

members must get permission to date, change jobs, or marry—or leaders specify what to dress, where to live, whether to have children, how to discipline children, and so on).

- The group is elitist, claiming unique, exalted status for itself, its leader(s), and its members (e.g., the leader is a special being, an avatar—or the organization and/or the leader are on a specific mission to rescue mankind).
- The group has a divided, us-versus-them mindset, which might lead to social strife.
- There are no authorities to whom the leader is accountable (unlike, for example, teachers, military commanders, or ministers, priests, monks, and rabbis of mainstream religious denominations).
- The organization teaches or suggests that its ostensibly lofty goals justify whatever tactics are required to achieve them. Members may engage in actions or activities that they would have regarded repugnant or unethical prior to joining the organization (e.g., lying to family or friends, or collecting money for bogus charities).
- In order to influence and manage members, the leadership creates sentiments of shame and/or guilt. Peer pressure and subtle types of persuasion are often used to accomplish this.
- Subservience to the leader or organization necessitates individuals severing links with family and friends, as well as drastically altering their own objectives and activities prior to joining.
- The organization is focused on recruiting new members.
- The members of the cult are often consumed with accruing money.

(from: Take Back Your Life: Recovering from Cults and Abusive Relationships, by Janja Lalich and Michael D. Langone)

Science Can't Afford to Pick and Choose Facts

For nearly two years now, the **Trends Journal** has been among a small band of voices and publications leading the way in pointing out inconvenient studies, events and facts in the face of a monolithic COVID "scientism."

That scientism has had little to do with the scientific method, which is all that can ever constitute actual science.

In the first wave of the purported pandemic, scientists sought to immediately discount inconvenient notions about the origin of the virus.

They dismissed reports by front-line doctors about protocols showing efficacy in treating COVID infections.

They proposed mask wearing and lockdown measures that were uncontroversially debunked by previous peer-reviewed studies.

They pretended to have answers where no research had been conducted, repeatedly presented policies that had no rigorous grounding in science, as being scientific.

When policies like "15 Days to Slow the Spread," "social distancing" and staying indoors failed miserably, they merely moved on to other even more draconian measures and dictates.

They flouted their own proscriptions. They profited obscenely by their power grabs.

Currently, they are pushing for compulsory injections of drugs that violate human rights and Constitutionally protected freedoms. The drugs don't work as advertised, aren't needed by the vast majority of people, and present dangers, especially to children who are almost immune from serious COVID effects.

"Science-based" COVID policies have led to increases in suicide, poverty, hunger and political instability that shows no sign of abating any time soon.

Practically every day for the last two years, some new strange affront to credulity is presented by authorities. One the latest this past week was a formal request by the FDA that the courts give them until 2076 to review and fully release the documents concerning the approval of the Pfizer BioNTech COVID-19 vaccine.

In an age where science wields more say over policies than ever, it's crucial that scientists who abuse their trust be held to account.

Specifically, Dr. Anthony Fauci, like his friend Bill Gates, has made himself a leader of a cult of science.

He has warped, discounted and tried to hide information and facts, and told admitted lies to promote supposedly nobly intended objectives.

When confronted on plain lies, he has resorted to demagoguery to avoid accountability.

If the good doctor is science, then science has thoroughly wrecked its own credibility, morphing into the worst cult of all.

For more on issues discussed here, see **Trends Journal** articles including:

- "'YOU CAN NEVER BE WOKE ENOUGH': HOW ELITES ARE CREATING A DISSOCIATIVE POPULACE" (22 Jun 2021)
- "HOW THE CCP WENT VIRAL ON THE WINGS OF COVID" (5 Oct 2021)

- "BATSH*T CRAZY: WUHAN WALLS CLOSING IN AROUND FAUCI" (18 May 2021)

YOUR CARBON CREDIT CARD HAS BEEN DECLINED

(First published on 23 Nov 2021 in the _Trends Journal_)

Get ready for a whole different kind of credit score.

This one has nothing to do with financial risk, and everything to do with control in the guise of combating "climate change."

A Swedish fintech company Doconomy is applying the "credit limit"model to calculations about pollution. It's issuing a new credit card called DO Black, which includes a feature to cut users off when their purchase amounts go over set CO_2 emission calculations for a given period.

"It's radical," Mathias Wikström, cofounder of Doconomy, commented to Fast Company, "but then again reducing CO_2 emissions [by] 50% by 2030 is quite radical, too."

The Agenda 2030 climate goal stems from a 2018 UN report which sounded fresh alarms about impending climate doom.

Various academic periodicals have published articles stressing the necessity for a "Personal Carbon Allowance," or PCA. Some claim that PCAs are the most effective way to combat climate change.

How might a PCA be used to combat climate change? Technocrats and politicians, who often use orders of magnitude more carbon than the average human being, are busy calculating limits based on "science."

Under their power grabbing schemes, mechanisms like limits on purchases, and how far that new Electric Vehicle (or even gas-powered) vehicle might be able to travel, would be implemented.

The Internet of Things (IoT), or networked computer control built into more and more everyday items, is a system that can be hijacked by authorities to meter and cut off usage of just about anything.

As an example, suppose you are allowed 10 Personal Carbon Allowance every day as an American (countries like China will no doubt be allotted more generous limits, but it is their century, after all).

If you've met your limit, forget about visiting an elderly relative that day, or ticking up the heat if it's a chilly evening.

With things like the DO Black credit card, the move is on to assign carbon costs to every human activity, and every commodity.

Sad to say, but blockchain and related Distributed Ledger Technologies (DLTs) are shaping up to be the perfect way to comprehensively track and apply the automatic cut-offs.

Every action and every object can be tokenized, authorized and de-authorized using such technologies.

In a world where people have largely rolled over and accepted lockdowns, vaccine mandates and vaccine passes for travel and entry to events and businesses, it's clear that elitists have no intention of observing any limits to their own desire to control and winnow away the bulk of humanity.

To them, your labor isn't needed. You're a useless eater, and unnecessary carbon emitter. And they are hell bent on doing something about the problem.

(for more on this topic, visit organicprepper.com)

CANCELED IN THE METAVERSE

(First published on 16 Nov 2021 in the *Trends Journal*)

Being canceled from Twitter or Facebook will seem quaint compared to the comprehensive way that people may disappear for all intents and purposes in the metaverse.

To understand the dangers, it's necessary to contemplate what the metaverse represents.

Where did "Metaverse" Come From?

Like so many technological realities, the metaverse was first envisioned in science fiction.

Neal Stephenson's 1992 novel *Snow Crash* coined the term in a story that involved avatars of people interacting with one another and AI entities in a three-dimensional virtual environment based on a metaphor of the real world.

Movies like *Avatar*, *The Matrix* and *Ready Player One* featured metaverse concepts.

The general idea is that the future of the internet won't involve interacting with a keyboard, flatscreen or mobile device. "Web 3.0" will literally exist around us, as a mixed reality of real and virtual objects, experiences, people and AI creatures.

The COVID War fueled the large-scale advent of the metaverse, via enforced shutdowns of real-world interactions that have characterized the whole history of human civilization.

The virtual worlds of hugely popular games like Fortnite have also been a factor.

Epic Games claimed in May 2020 that Fortnite had 350 million registered accounts and that players had spent 3.3 billion hours in-game in April 2020.

By various means, people are being conditioned to not only accept, but anticipate the "advantages" of virtual worlds where life-like interactions don't require physical proximity, and where virtually anything imaginable can be made part of new kinds of experience.

As far as the inevitability of the metaverse, Nasdaq.com recently reported that businesses that fail to realize the shift will be left in the dust:

> "Companies that ignore this emerging online marketplace will be left struggling in the same way that those who ignored the emergence of the world wide web and all that it implied were utterly hammered. For example, look up what happened to Kodak (KODK)."

Many might point out that the metaverse is not so much "mixed reality" as it is a nascent technological grand illusion.

But make no mistake, actions and experiences in the metaverse will have real consequences for human beings.

And mega tech entities such as Meta (formerly Facebook) currently positioning themselves to create and control the metaverse, may end up wielding powers that make their current platform "community guidelines" and censorship pale in comparison.

Meanwhile, an already burgeoning IOT (Internet Of Things) landscape is blurring the lines between the real and online world.

Journalist Susan Fourtane has detailed how an IOT might well act as a component of a nightmare "social credit" metaverse. She outlined several trends related to the IoS that are expected to become a reality by 2030:

1: Thoughts become action: using the brain as the interface, for example, users will be able to see map routes on VR glasses by simply thinking of a destination.

2: Sounds will become an extension of the devised virtual reality: users could mimic anyone's voice realistically enough to fool even family members.

3: Real food will become secondary to imagined tastes. A sensory device for your mouth could digitally enhance anything you eat, so that any food can taste like your favorite treat.

4: Smells will become a projection of this virtual reality so that virtual visits, to forests or the countryside for instance, would include experiencing all the natural smells of those places.

5: Total touch: Smartphones with screens will convey the shape and texture of the digital icons and buttons they are pressing.

6: Merged reality: VR game worlds will become indistinguishable from physical reality by 2030.

As John Whitehead of the Rutherford Institute noted, "this is the metaverse, wrapped up in the siren-song of convenience and sold to us as the secret to success, entertainment and happiness."

Mandated to Live in a New Reality

What happens when communication, imaginative creation and interaction become more and more comprehensively tied to AI systems and algorithms designed and dictated by corporate powers?

Quite simply, what one sees, hears, as well as what one is allowed to envision and communicate, is subject to the permissions built into the metaverse system.

And what's more, granular control (ie., control down to the level of the individual, and even specific actions, words, creative abilities, work activities, etc) will be far beyond what even the most traditional totalitarian systems that have existed in history could contemplate.

With a nod to Rod Serling:

Imagine trying to say something, and not only having a tweet removed, but no ability to even compose the sentence, or visualize the meme. Imagine having no access to verboten information, experiences or interactions in a new "mixed reality" which can effectively block anything it wants.

Imagine having to endure not just endless woke commercials, but having propaganda comprehensively integrated and woven into every aspect of daily experience.

Imagine being required not only to receive medical interventions and gene-level therapies, but being required to be implanted with transhuman metaverse technology that makes it impossible to escape seeing, experiencing, and being mandated to participate in an altered and comprehensively controlled reality.

Imagine that with the growing capabilities and "rights" afforded to Artificial Intelligence, this altered reality of a "metaverse" might not even be arbitrated by humans.

It should be obvious that the ability to play with reality in such a sophisticated way opens the door to the possibility of a 24/7 dystopian Twilight Zone that should give any sensible person pause.

Whitehead pointed out some of the dangers thusly:

> "The metaverse is, in turn, a dystopian meritocracy, where freedom is a conditional construct based on one's worthiness and compliance.

> "In a meritocracy, rights are privileges, afforded to those who have earned them. There can be no tolerance for independence or individuality in a meritocracy, where political correctness is formalized, legalized and institutionalized. Likewise, there can be no true freedom when the ability to express oneself, move about, engage in commerce and function in society is predicated on the extent to which you're willing to 'fit in.'"

Best Case: Metaverse Escapes the Big Tech Walls?

As with most things, a jealous regard for personal liberty, and for truths about the rights of men that stem not from the designs and creations of men, but the will of God, might go a long way in negotiating the metaverse.

Clearly, technological abilities and benefits that might ensue from easy access to data, richer sensory connections, and efficiencies in collaboration and work are selling points for building metaverses.

But no corporation or government should be allowed to assume control of the metaverse. Facebook changing its name to Meta, and launching a systematic plan and timetable for designing and controlling the terms of the metaverse must be watched closely.

Attempts by a few corporations to buy up talent and projects create de-facto metaverse monopolies, would be the worst possible outcome.

Advocates of freedom and human rights from every political spectrum would do well to come together in voicing a need for true diversity to be respected in the creation and adoption within the metaverse ecosystem.

If communities want to spin up worlds that freely attract participants, so be it. But no one should have the authority to ban or cancel metaverses that operate within Constitutional provisions that have crucially guaranteed real-world rights for generations.

And no one should ever be mandated to take part in a metaverse.

The **Trends Journal** has reported previously on some of the implications of the metaverse in articles including:

- "SINGULARITY UNIVERSITY: FUELING AI ASCENDANCE" (3 Aug 2021)
- "PULL THE PLUG ON TECH POWER OR THE PLUG WILL BE PULLED ON YOU" (24 Aug 2021)
- "POWERING OFF AI: THE NEXT 'HATE CRIME'" (14 Sep 2021)
- "INNOVEGA OFFERS A LOOKING GLASS INTO THE METAVERSE" (2 Nov 2021)

More thoughts on metaverse dangers can be found at the Rutherford Institute.

THE TECHNOCRACY'S WARPED REALITY FILTER

(First published on 11 Jan 2022 in the *Trends Journal*)

In current orthodoxy enforced by technocratic elites, the lines between what is celebrated and condemned reaches fresh heights of absurdity virtually every day.

Some latest examples came courtesy of a recent year-end article on MIT's technologyreview.com website, highlighting some of the "worst technology of 2021."

The article panned apps popular with children and teens that allow them to "refashion" their appearance in videos and pics.

It railed against "space tourism" excursions by billionaires.

And it excoriated a newly approved Alzheimer's pharmaceutical treatment for being exorbitantly expensive and having dangerous side effects.

The trouble with the MIT examples of bad technology, is that the same elites have championed technologies and policies that are analogous to all those mentioned, but far more devastating to society.

In short, the MIT year end review is a textbook example of a warped reality filter that elites routinely employ to push preferred narratives while inducing average people to ignore gaping hypocrisies.

Tilting at Tech Windmills

In a section about "Beauty Apps," the MIT article lays out the problem of apps that young people use to visually alter their appearance in videos and photos.

The article expresses concern that the apps provide the ability to do things like smooth the skin, thin noses, and enlarge eyes in digital images:

> *"These apps are not just gimmicks, like those that give you bunny ears. For some young women, they enforce false images they can't live up to. The message kids are getting is not 'Be yourself.'"*

The same MIT elites pointing out the dangers of apps that make no real physical changes to the human body, have no problem advocating "gender reassignment" surgery and hormone drug "therapy" for children.

In other words, utilizing drugs that dissolve the testicles of boys, performing radical mastectomies of teenage girls, and administering hormones that put the natural and healthy hormone balance of young men and women disastrously out of whack, are perfectly fine with the scientific conceits of MIT.

None of the pharmaceuticals, medical procedures and psychiatric and psychological opinions that have allowed radical physical disfigurement is considered a manifestation of "bad technology."

In fact, MIT has a whole section on their website explaining why they cover "Gender Confirmation Surgery." A page explains:

> *"MIT employees and their dependents who participate in an MIT medical plan are eligible for Coverage of Gender Confirmation Surgery (GCS), also known as Gender Reassignment Surgery (GRS), for the treatment of gender dysphoria.*

"What is GCS and Why is MIT Covering It? Gender Confirmation Surgery (GCS), also known as Gender Reassignment Surgery (GRS), is for the treatment of gender dysphoria. The prevailing position of the medical establishment is that GCS is a medically necessary procedure. The American Medical Association, the American Psychiatric Association and their Canadian counterparts support GCS as a medically necessary part of treatment for gender dysphoria and advocate the necessity of surgery and its coverage."

It's hard to fathom how the same voices attempting to gin up woke social outrage over "beauty apps" can defend far more destructive GCS without blinking an eye. But there it is.

Faux Space Jaunt Outcry

The excesses of billionaire's spending their money on "space tourism" was cited by the MIT year in review as another example of poor use of technology.

No doubt, hearing about Jeff Bezos playing Han Solo (if Han Solo were played by Yoda) is enough to make sensible average people shake their heads.

But the abuses of Amazon's platform, using its privileged algorithms and data gathering to illegally undermine businesses it purports to help, is far more consequential.

The **Trends Journal** detailed some of those abuses in articles including "AMAZON CAUGHT ILLEGALLY UNDERCUTTING COMPETITION" (19 Oct 2021) and "AMAZON USING DIGITAL BOOK DOMINANCE TO CENSOR" (16 Mar 2021).

Jeff Zuckerberg at Facebook (now META) funneled over 500 million into subverting the democratic prerogatives of average American citizen voters in 2020.

Apple, meanwhile, aided and conspired with the Communist Chinese government in order to gain a privileged business partnership.

None of those abuses by technocratic elites were cited as abhorrent examples of technology gone bad in 2021.

But "space tourism" made mention in the MIT article as a laser pinpoint meant to distract from the truly egregious abuses of Big Tech.

Cheap Therapeutics Helping Africa and India, Verboten in US

The MIT article spares no verbiage in lashing a big pharma Alzheimer's drug manufactured by Biogen as an example of bad technology.

The drug, Aduhelm, is cited for its yearly price tag of 56,400 dollars, and "substantial risk of serious brain swelling."

But while castigating the relatively obscure drug, MIT has proselytized for experimental COVID gene-level therapies, which have minted new pharma billionaires at Moderna and Pfizer.

The technology, deceptively likened to traditional vaccines in order to sell them to the public, have proved to be ephemeral as far as medical benefits.

They have also been associated with significant serious side effects including heart inflammation, especially affecting younger people otherwise at little risk of serious COVID complications.

In the roundup, MIT states:

> *"The best kind of medicine is inexpensive, safe, and effective. Think of setting a bone in a cast, filling a cavity, or administering a $2 polio vaccine. The worst medicine of 2021 is exactly the opposite."*

Whole regions of the world, including Africa and India proved in 2021 that anti-COVID protocols that employed early and prophylactic use of cheap, safe medicines including hydroxychloroquine and Ivermectin, showed benefit.

Frontline doctors in the U.S. and elsewhere repeatedly reported success in treating COVID by using antibiotics and other medicines and supplements.

But big pharma tied medical authorities, politicians, media and institutions like MIT all pushed COVID vaccines as the only solution.

That's not just an example of "worst technology." It's an indictment of the integrity of a thoroughly co-opted, propaganda focused technocracy.

And as a world-leading technological institution, MIT has more than done its part in the COVID propaganda war.

THIS WEEK IN SURVEILLANCE

INSURRECTIONISTS FAKE, COLLABORATIONISTS REAL. This past week Wonton Washington and the MSM tried to make the most of the anniversary of the January 6th protest.

But as it has been from the beginning, the real story is not "insurrectionists," but collaborationists.

Washington DC, and the rest of America, including the media, education and business, is full of willing dupes and active supporters of Chinese communists, and rancid Maoist ideology.

It's the key to understanding everything about "J6," the COVID War, the rabid animus against "America First," average Americans who value our traditions, Constitution and history…and yes, Donald Trump.

The view may sound conspiratorial. But it's actually so in the open, not to see it is the real Jedi mind trick.

Ties between the Communist Chinese regime and levers of power in the U.S. are so extensive they bubble up almost every day. Much like "Vichy France" served Nazi interests in the 1940's, America has become a vassal state of China.

Need a brief list of Chinese dupes and collaborationists? Start here:

- President Joe Biden and his son Hunter (compromised via numerous shady Chinese business and other dealings)
- Sen. Diane Feinstein (her "driver" a 20+ year spy working for the Communist Chinese)
- Rep. Eric Stalwell (literally sleeping with the enemy)
- Sen. Mitch Mconnell, married to the Chinese
- Neil Bush (head of a Chinese entity that has seen millions funneled between Chinese government interests and American business and political players)
- Anthony Fauci (reliable defender of Communist Chinese counterparts, and Congressional liar covering for the Wuhan lab origin of COVID)

- American Universities and Schools (dependant not only on Chinese foreign students, but on money funneled from the Chinese government to promote friendly views and "scholarship")
- Major American Media, bought off to disseminate Chinese friendly stories and propaganda
- Sports and Entertainment, led by the NBA and major Hollywood movie studios, working in a symbiotic business and propaganda relationship with the Chinese
- American corporations, led by the likes of Apple and Amazon, actively working with the Chinese not only to surveill and suppress their domestic population, but to bring Chinese communist style political repression to the U.S.

The U.S. Uniparty in Wonton Washington answers to China, period. Little wonder that in the aftermath of massive election irregularities in 2020, American intelligence agencies worked overtime to co-opt and direct a useful propaganda incident on January 6th.

Americans should never forget they have every right to rise up in popular protest for redress of grievances.

The minor law-breaking by average citizens on January 6th (much c it egged on by intelligence operatives) is literally nothing compared to the treasonous actions of the dupes and Collaborationists that continue to work overtime to bring down America.

The **Trends Journal** has detailed issues mentioned here in many other articles, including:

- "AMAZON HELPED XI SOLIDIFY GRIP ON CHINA" (21 De 2021)
- "UNIVERSITIES HIDING CCP CONFUCIUS INSTITUTES" (12 Oct 2021)

- "AMERICA DRIFTS TOWARD CHINA'S 'TECHNO-AUTOCRACY'" (9 Feb 2021)
- "CHINA WANTS A BULLET TRAIN INTO THE U.S." (1 Jun 2021)
- "CHINA BUSINESS ESPIONAGE NETS $500 BILLION A YEAR" (29 Jun 2021)
- "HOW THE CCP WENT VIRAL ON THE WINGS OF COVID" (5 Oct 2021)
- "U.S. MEDIA PUSHED NARRATIVE OF CHINA LOCKDOWN "SUCCESS" IN EARLY 2020" (27 Jul 2021)
- "APPLE BETRAYS CHINESE USERS FOR PROFIT" (1 Jun 2021)
- "AMERICA DRIFTS TOWARD CHINA'S 'TECHNO-AUTOCRACY'" (9 Feb 2021)
- "CHINA 'TALENT PROGRAM' GIFTED AT STEALING AMERICAN IP" (26 Oct 2021)
- "1984 TO 2021: HOW APPLE LEARNED TO LOVE BIG BROTHER" (17 Aug 2021)

MY COVID EXPERIENCE

(First published on 25 Jan 2022 in the _Trends Journal_)

Like many millions of others, it came my time to get COVID.

It happened to me before Christmas. It was less than a week after a great night dining out with Gerald Celente in Kingston. I thank God I wasn't feeling or showing any signs of sickness at that point.

But who knows? Gerald is one tough dude. He may well have already gotten COVID and shook it off with a sneeze or two. He's an amazing guy.

Anyway. My son, home from college, was a bit stuffed up one morning. Then we learned his girlfriend, a very sweet girl, who was vaccinated, had tested positive for COVID.

No one in our family, including my significant other Amy, nor our two children, had received any COVID vaccine.

My own reasons were based on what I knew, and much that I had written surrounding COVID.

Primarily, I judged that there was no way I would be taking an experimental gene-level "cure" from the same scientists that had literally funded and created the virus.

I never believed the bat soup story. Not for one second. The day I learned COVID occurred within spitting distance of a level IV virology lab in Wuhan, that's all I needed to know about the man-made origins of the virus.

As far as whether COVID was real or something made up, that was a bit more complicated. I believed it was real, and news of elderly people here in NY dying in droves in nursing homes, confirmed for me that COVID was at least something akin to a very bad flu.

I had personal experience in 2021 with several friends and family members diagnosed with COVID who experienced some of the odd symptoms, including complete loss of smell, chronic headaches, etc.

An Incident With My Brother

And then one night this past summer my sister-in-law called me. She said my brother George had gotten COVID. Close to 60, and 2 days less than a year older than me (yes, my Irish twin!) my stoic brother hadn't revealed to anyone what he was battling.

He had apparently gotten over the worst phase, during which he dropped a good thirty pounds. George is a big boned man, and had been overweight during latter years, but he had lost a significant amount of weight a few years before this. So he was not anything like morbidly obese.

But according to my sister-in-law, George was now suffering mental effects from COVID that were making him paranoid. I frankly didn't believe it, and thought the two must have just been arguing about something.

I asked to speak to my brother.

"They're all COVID crazy," George said to me when he got on the phone. "They want to put me in the hospital. They all got the vax! I told them, I'm fine, I'm not going to the hospital."

"Okay buddy, do you need to maybe just get away, and spend a night or two at my place?"

"Yeah," he replied. "That sounds good."

George and his wife live about 45 minutes away from me. We decided to meet in Poughkeepsie. George's wife drove him, and she called me as I was on the road.

"Joe, he just tried to grab the steering wheel. He thinks I'm driving too fast. I'm driving literally 20 miles an hour, but he won't let me drive."

I asked her to put my brother on the phone.

"George, what's up?"

"She's driving dangerous. She's trying to get us killed. Honey, slow down," I could hear him warn my sister-in-law.

It happened to be raining pretty hard. But still, I knew my sister-in-law was a very responsible person who would not be barreling along, especially given my brother's apparent nervousness.

George actually made her pull over. I talked to him, and convinced him to let her get back on the road. I told him I'd stay on the phone with him.

I tried to engage him in a little small talk about baseball, knowing he's always been a big Mets fan.

"Honey, slow down. Just keep your eyes on the road. Slow."

"George, I'm driving fifteen miles an hour."

"Just slow down. You're going to get in an accident."

It was very weird. It was like my brother couldn't break away from obsessing about getting in an accident, and going too fast, though it was obvious to me at this point that his wife was literally crawling along Route 9W.

They eventually got to the meet-up spot in Poughkeepsie where I was waiting, which happened to be just across the way from Saint Francis Hospital.

"George, I gotta tell you. You don't sound quite yourself," I told him, as we stood in the parking lot in the rain.

"Don't tell me my own brother is COVID crazy too," he shook his head, and I felt horrible. But I also knew the man wasn't behaving rationally. He said some other odd things, including getting names of places wrong. It just wasn't like him.

Overall, he was markedly more talkative than usual, defensive and strangely derogatory toward everyone, suspicious, but also acidly quick-witted in a manner that was very unlike him.

"Buddy, I wouldn't say this if I didn't love you and want the best for you, but you don't seem quite yourself. Do you think it might be a good idea to maybe go to Saint Francis and have them check you out?"

George ended up letting us take him to the emergency room at Saint Francis. He was admitted, and doctors ended up determining he was experiencing COVID related brain inflammation. He was given medication for it, and after a few days he was back home and doing better.

Talking to him, I could tell immediately this was the "old George," affable, not paranoid, nor exhibiting the strange talk that he had that night.

I told Gerald at the time about what I observed with my brother.

"COVID is definitely some strange malady," I remarked. "This whole thing is crazy, because the world is between a rock and a hard place. This virus is real. But this gene-level shit they're trying to get everyone to take is bad news."

Armed With Info Gathered From Reporting

Writing for the **Trends Journal**, I had a very good pulse on the virus, the vaccines, what front-line physicians like Doctor Zelenko over in Orange County, not far from where I lived, were recommending, etc.

When I first bought some boxes of "Horse Ivermectin" from Amazon, they were five dollars each. They went up to 25. Then 80 dollars for two boxes. By November, the U.S. Postal service was working with authorities to intercept packages and stop people from getting any.

I had already seen NAC (N-Acetyl-Cysteine), a supplement I used pretty routinely to reduce phlegm, which I'm prone to, banned from sale at places like Amazon.

Apparently, people had learned that NAC helps with congestion brought on by COVID.

I quickly sourced NAC elsewhere, and bought a supply. Again, what had been a six dollar supplement was now selling for over 20 dollars a bottle.

Between hydroxychloroquine, Ivermectin, NAC and even aspirin, the discounting of vitamins C and D, and the insistence by many medical professionals that antibiotics should not be used in the treatment of COVID, it was clear to me there was something truly evil going on with the medical establishment in concert with governmental authorities.

Even if Ivermectin or hydroxychloroquine were not believed to have any special benefit in treating COVID, during all of 2020 and a good portion of early 2021, there were no vaccines even available to people.

Why were these drugs being suppressed and lied about?

They had been used routinely by millions of people for maladies like malaria, lupus, and getting rid of parasites, and were completely uncontroversial and proven safe. "Right to Try," for patients, and the right of doctors to prescribe "off-label" uses of such drugs, should have prevailed.

Instead, there were vicious propaganda wars being waged against the drugs, and any doctors advocating their use.

The antibiotics angle regarding COVID was just as bizarre. In February 2021 I wrote the **Trends Journal** story "BACTERIAL PNEUMONIA & COVID: WHAT THE CDC SAYS."

The facts were straightforward. Whenever viral pneumonia is present, there's a good statistical chance it can turn into bacterial pneumonia. And treatment with antibiotics is standard treatment for bacterial pneumonia.

In other words, utilizing antibiotics for COVID treatment, as Doctor Zelenko and others were advocating, made complete sense.

Why were doctors waiting until people were congested and dying, and then putting them on ventilators? Why weren't people being treated in a timely way with antibiotics for pneumonia?

I myself have always been prone to lung related ailments, including bronchitis and walking pneumonia, which I had both as a child and an adult (once in the middle of summer, which was particularly miserable).

I vowed that if I did contract COVID, I would make sure I was prescribed Augmentin, an antibiotic I knew worked for me in combating past bouts with lung infections.

COVID On Christmas

So, it was getting close to Christmas. I had just finished putting together a holiday-themed cartoon project called _The Fiddle Faddles Christmas Special_. I'd created it as a sort of retro-style feel good story, about an elderly couple who find out their kids won't be home for the holidays.

I was especially delighted that Gerald took a cameo role in the video.

A few days after showing the final video to some friends and voice actors who had contributed to the project, my son was sniffling. He's of notably good constitution, and it takes a lot to set him down.

Whatever he had was just a minor inconvenience to him. But then we learned the news about his girlfriend receiving a positive COVID test. And sure enough, within a few days, I was feeling fatigued, and so was Amy, my significant other.

At first, symptoms seemed manageable enough. I even laughed when I discovered that yep, my sense of smell (and taste) were going rapidly. One morning, I could barely smell the scent of cinnamon, which I liked to put in my cereal. The next day, I couldn't smell any scent from the cinnamon bottle, or anything else at all.

The next two weeks were progressively worse on every physical front. If this was the mild Omicron, I could only thank God that He had kept me from contracting Delta.

I was feverish, with temperature spikes to 103. Doses of ibuprofen barely kept it under control. I of course pulled out a box of that Ivermectin I'd purchased before the suppressions and bans.

Nothing I say here constitutes medical advice, of course. I'm simply conveying what I chose to do for myself.

After 10 days, I was definitely not doing better. Neither was Amy. We made a call to urgent care.

Assuming the call was basically like a tele-visit with a doctor, I related my basic situation and symptoms, as well as my history of susceptibility to lung ailments.

"I think I just need some Augmentin, which works well for me when I have pneumonia, which I know I have," I told the doctor.

"Well, I'm not prescribing Augmentin for you," he replied. There was a smugness in the way he said it that ticked me off.

"Why not?" I questioned.

"Because that's not a treatment for COVID," he answered.

"So what am I supposed to do? Wait until I'm ready to be put on a ventilator?" I felt my blood boiling.

"You have a nice night," by God as my witness the man seemed to be making a special effort to convey: *well you opted not to get vaccinated, it serves you right.*

"Fuck off," I said to him, before he hung up.

Amy let me know I'd probably not done myself any good with that one.

The next morning, she decided to go to Urgent Care in person. I told her I would see what they did in her case, before I went.

She returned more than six hours after having left. She had to literally stand out in the rain for forty minutes in a line along with other sick people, in temps just above freezing, just to get on a list to be seen.

Why the hell couldn't these people have been allowed to wait in a hallway of the place?

After getting placed on the list, she was sent back to her car to wait hours in the parking lot, before being called in.

Thankfully, after a positive COVID test and an X-ray of her lungs, she was prescribed two antibiotics. Including Augmentin.

The next morning, it was my turn to go in person to Urgent Care. I was on line at around 8 in the morning. Barely able to stand, congested and short of breath, I leaned against a cold wall.

There was nothing to do except stand there for thirty minutes, before being queried by a nurse and put on the day's list, and sent to go wait in my car.

When I was examined for a scant two hours later, the presiding doctor told me my lungs sounded clear.

"I'd like an x-ray," I answered. "My partner has pneumonia, and I'm sure something's going on with me."

After the x-ray, the doctor returned. "The x-ray does show pneumonia developing."

From there, it was thankfully no issue getting Augmentin and a second antibiotic, as well as a steroid to treat inflammation. I also tested positive for COVID, and negative for the flu.

Slow Road Toward Recovery

Christmas was gone, and New Year's was too. I was six or seven days into treatment, and still utterly fatigued, aching, experiencing fevers and chills, waking up soaked with night sweats, and so on.

Unlike my son, my constitution has never been what anyone would call super robust. From a young age, I've always tried to compensate by eating healthy, and trying my best to stay in shape.

Amy, who my son takes after as far as general constitution, seemed a little further along, but she was by no means out of the woods either.

Odd symptoms were manifesting for both of us. In my case, my eyes were not focusing normally, and were very sensitive to light. I was also experiencing headaches virtually every morning by 4 am, and I've never been prone to headaches.

The hiatus from contributing to the **Trends Journal** was almost over, since the magazine was scheduled to go out again after the holiday break.

Gerald, as he always is, was incredibly solicitous the whole way, offering help in any manner he could. He let us know that if we weren't up to trying to get the magazine out, it would just have to wait.

We told him we thought we could get through a gameday, and thankfully we did.

At this point, as I sit here writing this (overlong!) missive on 20 January, I'm finally feeling close to okay. I'm extremely deconditioned. But my lungs are clear. The headaches have abated. Smell and taste have returned. Eyes are still sensitive.

Along the way, there was another course of "horse" Ivermectin, which I believe greatly helped and felt the effects of, after only a day or two. There was also plenty of garlic, vitamins C and D, Quercetin with Zinc supplements, Oil of Oregano, raw onion sandwiches, and anything else I could think of to throw at this thing.

Amy, who has a much harder time remaining idle than I do (I can lay on a couch and watch favorite Rifftrax or MST3K episodes ad nauseum), has actually been battling through some relapse fatigue. Leg aches, heaviness in her chest, and other persisting symptoms haven't been pleasant. But she too seems to be over the worst hump of COVID.

To anyone who believes COVID is made up, has never been uniquely sequenced, etc., all I can say is that from experience with others, and via my own experience, I know that this ailment includes symptoms that are unlike anything I've previously heard of, or ever had with any flu or bout of bronchitis or pneumonia.

To me, it just confirmed that COVID is unfortunately a very real phenomenon, and can hit people who are of a certain age or certain constitution very hard.

The good news is that pretty standard treatments and supplements can make a difference, as front-line doctors of integrity know and continue to proclaim.

The fact that getting some of those treatments has been so difficult and complicated by frankly evil agendas of batshit crazy technocratic elites (see my touchstone article from May 2021 "BATSH*T CRAZY: WUHAN WALLS CLOSING IN AROUND FAUCI"), unbound genetic experimenters, and pandemic profiteers, represents a low point in the annals of human history. And that's saying something.

As far as the experimental vaccines? The huge numbers of serious adverse effects have been noted consistently in the **Trends Journal**. Even on Twitter, many thousands of people are expressing regrets about taking the vaccines, as reported recently by dailyveracity.com.

Thanks To A Man Made For These Times

Also heartening is the fact that many people around the world have woken up thanks to the COVID saga. They are marching in the streets in nation after nation. From Europe to Australia to Canada, and even in far too lazy America, millions have stood against vaccine mandates and lockdown orders.

And battles are being won. Britain just dropped their mandate regime. The U.S. Supreme Court at least partially struck down Joe Biden's unprecedented and unconstitutional vax mandate.

Authoritarians and those bent on playing God deciding the medical and even genetic fate of humans, are being called out, and examined more closely as a result of the big lie that is failing more badly with each passing day.

No one believes Fauci any more about his bat tales and gain-of-function funding denials. God willing, he will be brought to justice for crimes against humanity.

And hopefully so will many others, for the tragic nursing home deaths of the elderly, for the devastation of a young generation who will never completely escape the scars of what they have been put through, for the economic catastrophe causing want and starvation, for the destruction of small businesses and average livelihoods, and for the obscene self-enrichment of already scofflaw elites.

At the end of the day, I'm proud to have made some small contributions to Gerald Celente's monumental and historically important work and voice at the **Trends Journal**.

I'm also proud of every reader who supports what is being done here, and I hope you all continue to spread the word, to keep fighting for what's right, and to use the information you find here to equip yourself to deal with whatever the future brings.

My grandmother Connie Traina used to say to me when I was young, "if you have your health, you have everything."

Gerald Celente is a man who not only exudes the good health that my Sicilian grandmother did for all of her 91 years on earth. He is dedicated to informing as many people as possible about how to live, as Tom Wolfe might've put it, a "life in full."

The efforts of men like him continue to throw a huge gut punch into even the best laid plans and machinations of powerful, supercilient, craven and just plain evil actors on the world stage.

God bless him, the COVID War could not have found a better Man of Peace to wage the good fight.

ELITES ARE THE PROBLEM THAT MUST BE FACED

(First published on 1 Feb 2022 in the *Trends Journal*)

It's past time to go after monied elites.

Fueled by a stranglehold on modern technology and virtually all major institutions in society, their power is unprecedented in modern history.

And it's being corruptly leveraged to accrue more power, while undermining the will not only of average Americans, but of citizens in democracies all over the world.

If the COVID pandemic has proven anything, it's that those who can are likely to exploit (or even create) crises to gain advantage from them.

COVID has been an elite driven crisis. Popular will and opinion, repeated mass demonstrations against lockdowns and forced business closures and restrictions, and vaccine passes and mandates, have been opposed by a relatively tiny cabal of power-grabbing dictatorial leaders.

And of course, they haven't lived by the rules and rationales they've proscribed for others. A Twitter user Freespirit963 recently noted:

> *"The elite class wears masks for photo ops.*
>
> *"The middle class wears masks on airplanes and on the walk from the restaurant door to the table.*
>
> *"The working class wear masks on the bus to work, all day at work, and on the bus home from work."*

Whatever this is, It's not democracy.

By now, it has been thoroughly documented how mega rich billionaires virtually doubled their wealth from 2020 to the present moment.

That's right. Jeff Bezos, Bill Gates, Elon Musk, George Soros, Mike Bloomberg and dozens of the world's richest made all the right moves as COVID pandemic profiteers.

But a class of rich below the very richest also gained disportionately during COVID.

All that profiteering reversed a trend during the Trump years up to the time that the COVID virus made its debut. According to factcheck.org, not exactly a conservative data clearinghouse, even counting 2020, all of the following benefited the middle and working classes under Trump (all numbers in comparison to the previous Obama administration):

- Median household income: up 6 percent
- Real Weekly Earnings: up 8.7 percent
- Home Ownership: up 2.1 points (especially important, given that home prices rose 27.5 percent)
- Poverty Rate: down 1.3 points

Considering the virtual grind to a halt of economic activity during most of 2020, those numbers, and others, are especially impressive.

The rich got richer during the Trump years. But the percentage gains of the "paycheck" classes were higher, and that, as much as anything, was a remarkable definer of what made Trump so popular with that group.

COVID—or more specifically, the policies enacted to deal with the virus—destroyed that dynamic, of course.

And of course, President Trump was fully responsible for those policies. He could've fired COVID czar Anthony Fauci as soon as he learned Fauci oversaw funding and research connections with the Wuhan lab that government intelligence knew was a possible source of the virus breakout.

Trump paid for disastrous COVID related decisions with his presidency. Of course, there were other miscalculations. The President focused on drawing big crowds compared to Biden's anemic public showings, thinking energizing his base would win the day.

Meanwhile, operators like Mark Zuckerburg, Jack Dorsey, Klaus Schwab and Laurene Powell Jobs were using their power and money to radically change voting laws and control and suppress the free flow of information during the election cycle.

Holding Elites To Their Own Lofty Woke Standards

It's time for leadership that targets elites as the highest priority, front-and-center issue and danger to the world that they are.

America needs a 21st century tech and politics savvy Teddy Roosevelt, if you will.

Whether from the political right, center, or left, an opportunity is there for someone to step up and start proposing how the bottom 90 percent can grab back some power from the world's richest.

Beyond guillotines and straight-up confiscations, there are all sorts of creative initiatives that crusaders can probably come up with that would have popular appeal, and be very hard for people who think of themselves as "progressive" and "woke" to resist.

Here are a few ideas, off the cuff:

A "Small and Start-Up Business COVID Recovery Fund":
This would be paid for by confiscating money from the top 1000 wealthiest Americans. Or maybe the top 2000, or the top 5-percent, or 10-percent.
With spiraling inflation, being a millionaire isn't what it used to be. Fine. Include "hundred millionaires" and up.

The legislation could include formulas determining how much these wealthy profited over the course of COVID, compared to their pre-COVID inflows, and take ALL of it, to fund recovery for small business.

Of course, the government will thoroughly screw up, and the program will be riddled with corruption.

But, having lost a considerable chunk of their wealth, perhaps elites choose to have their mouthpiece organs of social and traditional media to actually point out how corrupt and badly the program is going. Having oligarchs and politicians actually warring with each other, as opposed to colluding against the rest of us, would be a step in the right direction.

Transition of Critical Tech Infrastructure into the Public Trust (Ownership): This could include sectors of the economy, like backbone internet companies. Heck, it could include Amazon, the de facto internet marketplace platform, with nearly half of all online buying, and Google, with a similar chunk of advertising control.

Throw in Meta and Twitter, with their duo monopoly on social communication.

No need to have the government actually run the companies.

Oversee an initiative to use blockchain technology to restructure these corporations into Decentralized Autonomous Organizations (DAOs) that benefit the American people, and not the elites who have thoroughly abused laws and political connections to build and grow their corporate empires.

Issue non-transferrable NFTs (Non-Fungible Tokens) that pay out dividends to citizens. Sell it as that "Universal Basic Income" so near and dear to the stated aspirations of the woke.

These are companies that represent more wealth than virtually 3/4ths of the world's national economies. They have abused that tremendous power to render themselves largely unaccountable to government authorities.

It has to change.

"Power To People Voting Reform": George Soros made news this past week for donating 125 million dollars to the Democrat Party.

It's being called the largest political donation of its kind to date. That's arguable, considering the 500-plus million dollars Mark Zuckerburg spent co-opting the 2020 election cycle.

That kind of corrosive, distorting influence screams out for reform.

It's time to limit campaign contributions. For a given election cycle or year, maximum contributions to candidates or parties could be limited to some percentage of the median income Americans earned in the previous year.

In 2020, the median household income was $67,521.

Individuals could be limited to contributing no more than five percent of that overall median number to any one candidate, and to contributing only to candidates for whom they can directly cast votes.

As for donations from entities other than individual voters? End them. No donations allowed from corporations, unions, PACs, etc. Only individuals can vote. Only individuals can make a political donation.

Reform could go further. Only candidates run for an office. If only candidates, and not parties, could receive a donation. Parties would not necessarily wither away, though they would surely lose a huge amount of their current power.

They might be less partisan and more sustained by substantive policy ideas and beliefs. It could hardly be any worse for the country than it is now.

To those who read all this and think going after elites will devolve into a French, or even worse, a Russian Revolution, the answer is—that's a possibility and a risk.

Fortunately, the country has something that France and Russia lacked in their revolutions, that allows for real reform while making sure Americans retain equal protection under the law.

It's called the Constitution. Follow its letter and spirit, and the tyranny of monied tyrants, our present-day "kings," can be dealt with in a way that enlarges the franchise and the freedom of average Americans.

Elites are the problem. It's time for "We The People" to wield our own power to focus on and deal with the problem, and hopefully restore a balance to the Republic.

For more on issues touched on in this article, see:

- "ZUCKERBERG BOUGHT 2020 ELECTION WITH HALF A BILLION" (19 Oct 2021)
- "A MODEST TAX PROPOSAL FOR BILLIONAIRES" (3 Aug 2021)
- "PULL THE PLUG ON TECH POWER OR THE PLUG WILL BE PULLED ON YOU" (24 Aug 2021)
- "BILLIONAIRE TAX SCOFFLAWS PLOW SAVINGS INTO WEBS OF CONTROL" (15 Jun 2021)
- "PORTALS OF POWER: HOW MEGA BILLIONAIRES USURP ELECTIVE BODIES" (11 May 2021)
- "BILL GATES, PHILANTHRO-PREDATOR" (21 Sep 2021)
- "WEF LAUNCHES NEW ASSAULT AGAINST AMERICAN BILL OF RIGHTS" (13 Jul 2021)
- "HOW BIG TECH MAINTAINS ITS MONOPOLY" (17 Aug 2021)
- "AMAZON CAUGHT ILLEGALLY UNDERCUTTING COMPETITION" (19 Oct 2021)
- "TECHNOCRATS WIDEN WEALTH GAP THANKS TO PANDEMIC" (13 Apr 2021)
- "COVID WAR: RICH GOT RICHER, POOR GOT POORER" (21 Sep 2021)

GOV'T AI WILL TRACK AUTHOR "FINGERPRINTS" TO CRUSH DISSENT

(First published on 15 Feb 2022 in the _Trends Journal_)

Artificial intelligence which can track written materials back to their authors, by identifying unique "fingerprint" traits of authorship, is being rapidly developed by the U.S. government.

That's according to Nextgov, a consortium of leading tech corps that works closely with government agencies, developing, selling and procuring technology.

The revelation is especially troubling, given the growing use of the U.S. Intelligence apparatus and other government assets to trample the Constitutional rights and freedoms of American citizens.

According to Nextgov, which was pre-briefed on the author fingerprint project, the Department of Homeland Security said it could be used to strip the possibility of anonymity from written communications.

Not surprisingly, a spokesperson talking about the project alluded to the safety of children as a leading use case for the technology.

"This effort, we think, is potentially game-changing for tracking disinformation campaigns, and things like combating human trafficking and other malicious activities that go on in online text forums, and elsewhere using text," Dr. Timothy McKinnon told Nextgov.

McKinnon is the Intelligence Advanced Research Projects Activity (IARPA) program manager of HIATUS, which stands for Human Interpretable Attribution of Text Using Underlying Structure.

IARPA is a research hub for the U.S. Intelligence Community.

HIATUS is being developed to work both ways, noted McKinnon. It will be able to trace authorship back to any person, or even AI machines that write a given document. It will also be able to disguise written communications to shield authorship.

McKinnon explained:

> *"With attribution, what we're doing is we're identifying stylistic features. So, this is like signs of blank word placement syntax that can identify who wrote a given text. Think about it as like your written fingerprint, right? What characteristics make your writing unique? So the technology would be able to identify that fingerprint compared against a corpus of other documents, and match them up if they are from the same author," he explained. "On the privacy side, what the technology would do is it would figure out ways that text could be modified so that it no longer looks like a person's writing."*

"We're looking to develop systems that can be robustly performant across diverse domains and genres of text—and also, there's going to be foreign languages involved in the program as it progresses as well," McKinnon said.

Netgov notes that IARPA has a developmental role in tech, and doesn't have much of a role deploying or operationalizing the technology it creates. The "tools" it creates are distributed to intelligence agencies to implement based on their own purposes and judgment.

DHS Already Casting American Free Speech Rights As Terrorism

Just last Monday, the Department of Homeland Security issued a terrorist alert bulletin, warning of a "heightened threat environment."

The cause? A "proliferation of false or misleading narratives" regarding COVID-19.

The DHS lamented that the unapproved thoughts and information provided by outlets not toadying to the government line are weakening "public faith in government institutions."

In the alert, the agency also cited "calls for violence" and threats from foreign terror organizations:

> *"The United States remains in a heightened threat environment fueled by several factors, including an online environment filled with false or misleading narratives and conspiracy theories, and other forms of mis- dis- and mal-information (MDM) introduced and/or amplified by foreign and domestic threat actors..."*

The DHS focus on demonizing the free speech rights of Americans was another breathtaking escalation in the government's war against domestic dissent.

It came on the heels of the President adding his administration's voice to the recent attempted canceling of Joe Rogan, the world's leading podcaster, for Rogan's COVID wrongthink.

White House Press Secretary Jen Psaki has urged Spotify, a music streaming service with exclusive rights to "The Joe Rogan Experience," to censor the show.

In response, Spotify pulled over a hundred episodes of the program from access.

Despite that, Rogan this past week claimed Spotify has "stood by me," during the controversy, and said he's considering a 100 million dollar from the surging Rumble video platform.

Rumble, along with GAB, have emerged as "free speech" alternatives to big tech platforms that have increasingly banned and censored dissident voices, often with illegal prodding from Congress, which is explicitly barred by the Constitution with infringing the free speech rights of Americans.

No HIATUS From the US Government Domestic Spy Network

With HIATUS, U.S. Intelligence will have a new weapon in its arsenal to spy out and neutralize dissident voices.

It will be used in the name of protecting children, protecting the health of Americans, ensuring safety, and various other tropes.

But make no mistake, its real purpose will be to suppress, and if necessary, crush popular uprisings against government policies which are robbing citizens of their wealth and freedoms, all to the benefit of a tiny cabal of technocratic and political elites.

For related articles, see:

- "GOVERNMENT: FREE SPEECH IS BAD FOR YOUR HEALTH" (21 Sep 2021)
- "REUTERS 'EXCLUSIVE' CROWS ABOUT BIG TECH MERGING WITH U.S. INTEL TO TARGET POLITICAL DISSIDENTS" (27 Jul 2021)
- "U.S. GOVERNMENT CROSSING THE CONSTITUTIONAL LINE" (23 Feb 2021)
- "Censorship 2019" (11 Dec 2018)

ZUCKERBERG: AI WILL PLAY GOD IN YOUR METAWORLD

(First published on 1 Mar 2022 in the *Trends Journal*)

Under the guise of "human rights," Artificial Intelligence (AI) will decide what can take place in the metaverse-or at least Meta's (formerly Facebook) version of it.

Zuckerberg gave a new demonstration this past week of metaverse technology his company is building.

Together with a tech engineer, he showed how an "empty" virtual space could be filled and created into an island paradise, via voice commands to an AI intelligence.

Saying things like, "Actually, let's go to the beach," "let's add some clouds," and having landscape and ocean appear, along with a sky and cumulous accents, the corporate billionaire commented admiringly, "that's all AI generated."

True, the graphics involved looked like something from a first generation Wii game system.

But Meta is clearly focused on the AI and interfacing technologies that will connect and allow communication and "world-building." More realistic graphics will come later. So will sensors and wearables that give users tactile sensations, providing a more "immersive" experience.

The presentation made it seem like anything one desired and could imagine would be available by merely speaking it to an AI genie that Zuckerberg referred to as "Builder Bot."

If that sounds like something out of a children's TV show, it may not be a mistake. Meta's infantilizing version of the metaverse will come with a huge caveat: just like in the classic 1960's sitcom *I Dream Of Jeannie*, the wish giver will be the one really in charge.

To put it bluntly, there are things Meta's metaverse won't allow. Think of those vague "community guidelines" that instill corporate-government narratives and mete out punishments and, if necessary, outright bans to dissident viewpoints and thoughts.

During the demonstration, Zuckerberg couched the implementation of all his ideological biases by a "Builder Bot" as ensuring "human rights."

But the fast evolving Meta spin up of a virtual world is already inherently unequal, with all the power weighted to a central authority: a corporation, a mega billionaire, and a Federal government which has fully partnered in the monopolistic ascendency of a handful of tech corporations in America.

Zuckerberg himself has said that he believes the Metaverse is destined to be the "the next version of the Internet."

In the same way that the relatively open internet of the 1900's gradually gave way to the dominance of a handful of powerful tech social and commerce platforms, Meta's mega billionaire wants to position Meta as the mediator of that new internet.

No one should be surprised. And a recent ZDNet article underscores that no one should want a part of it:

> *"In a Metaverse, as conceived by Meta CEO Mark Zuckerberg, you cannot even scratch your virtual nose without the permission of a program controlled completely by the company."*

Part of the promise of so-called "Web3" or decentralized internet technologies is that users will control their own digital destiny.

Whether it's how one chooses to store and use the value of one's entrepreneurial efforts, investments and labor, or one's digital property, or even one's digital identity, there are decentralized blockchain initiatives envisioning and building new paradigms and new solutions.

It's not an exaggeration to say that many of these initiatives, while still very in their infancy, are already disrupting the current status quo of the corporate and government control that has exerted a progressive lock and key on such things in the modern and current digital age.

Whatever else the metaverse will be, it is already shaping up to be a battleground of control and freedom that everyone should be paying attention to, since literally future reality is literally at stake.

For more on issues surrounding the metaverse, check out:

- "METAVERSE: THE NEW COLLECTIVE" (14 Dec 2021)
- "METAWORLD" 2022 Top Trend (30 Nov 2022)
- "CANCELED IN THE METAVERSE" (16 Nov 2021)
- "METAVERSE AND NFTS ONLY GETTING HOTTER" (2 Nov 2021)

AI MENTAL HEALTH "INTERVENTIONS" ABOUT TO GET REAL

(First published on 8 Mar 2022 in the _Trends Journal_; republished in WinePress News)

You're on your favorite news forum, or social media platform.

A post or piece of news catches your attention. It gets your juices going. You have something you want to say, share, question or rant about.

So you type away.

And then a message pops up. You've exhibited signs of a mental health issue. You're being asked to proceed with further digital screening, after which you'll be given helpful information about where to go for further help.

In some cases, "help" may be coming to you.

The above scenario is the next step of corporate-government overseers in using "health" dangers to impose authoritarian suppression of dissident viewpoints.

And the framework for its implementation is being assembled right now, via government agencies including the CDC, political bodies including Congress and the Biden administration, and tech companies and leading university research programs.

Dartmouth Develops AI Driven "Mental Health" Tech

Dartmouth University last week showcased an Artificial Intelligence powered system that researchers claim can identify "mental problems" of users participating in online discussion forums.

The AI system reportedly utilizes an emphasis on emotions rather than the exact substance of the social media messages being studied in its approach.

The researchers say the technique works better over time, regardless of the themes mentioned in the postings. Their work was encapsulated in a paper presented at the 20th International Conference on Web Intelligence and Intelligent Agent Technology.

According to Xiaobo Guo, a co-author of the paper, the Dartmouth research, which was developed using Reddit forum posts as inputs, is meant to potentially help in identifying and intervening in cases where "mental health" problems might warrant.

Guo noted that people tend not to seek care for mental health illnesses for a variety of reasons, including stigma, excessive fees, and a lack of access to resources.

Guo said the Dartmouth AI technology being developed might be used to "prompt" users, and that via an alert, they might be more receptive or inclined to seek assistance with AI identified mental health issues.

He also said digital screening technologies might play a part in a process, where admittedly posters were not seeking help, or a medical or mental health diagnosis by their online activities on forums.

"Social media offers an easy way to tap into people's behaviors. The data is voluntary and public, published for others to read," said Guo.

Invasive Technology, Political Danger

Of course, the Dartmouth researchers fail to acknowledge that people posting those "public comments" aren't doing so to authorize a mental health screening, much less an intervention.

If that isn't ominous itself, the progressive political distortion of what counts as a mental health issue, in the age of MAGA, COVID, and now the Russia and Ukraine conflict, raises the specter of even more political suppression than is already the case via technocratic and government collusion.

The suppression and smearing of dissidents as mentally disturbed is a common feature of totalitarian regimes. It's happening more frequently in supposed Western democracies that claim to value freedom of thought and conscience.

As the **Trends Journal** has pointed out in previous recent articles, a dangerously politicized CDC is already weaponizing "health dangers" to erode first and second amendment rights to free speech and self-defense. For more on that, see "GOVERNMENT: FREE SPEECH IS BAD FOR YOUR HEALTH" (21 Sep 2021) and "UPDATE: FREE SPEECH IS BAD FOR YOUR HEALTH" (5 Oct 2021).

During the COVID War, the government, including the CDC and Congress actively coordinated with and pressured social media platforms to suppress and censor dissident viewpoints concerning COVID policies and official narratives, under the guise of combating "health misinformation."

CDC Director Rachel Walensky has also gone on record advocating restrictions on gun ownership rights by cherry-picking statistics and declaring a gun related "health crisis."

Now, with the frenzy of propaganda being furiously arrayed against Russia, people expressing opinions or information contrary to the government's war narrative, might have even more to worry about than merely being smeared as Russian operatives.

They might qualify as mentally deranged, certified by dispassionate, "scientific" AI.

By a veneer of official sanction by authorities like the CDC, prevailing political orthodoxy, and sophisticated tech engineered at leading universities, the political perversion of "science" to justify suppression of "dangerous speech" is likely to accelerate.

And systems like Dartmouth's AI social media mental health screening technology may well serve as a potent weapon in the technocracy's arsenal.

Made in the USA
Monee, IL
06 December 2022

19947617R00157